OLAV GJÆREVOLL
REIDAR JØRGENSEN

# MOUNTAIN FLOWERS
## OF SCANDINAVIA

ILLUSTRATIONS
BY
DAGNY TANDE LID

THIRD EDITION

ISBN 82-7028-449-1

EDITED BY TRONDHJEMS TURISTFORENING
F. BRUNS BOKHANDELS FORLAG
TRONDHEIM 1978
KELLER & TOFT A/S

# CONTENTS

Preface.......................... 2
Mountains and Mountain Flowers....... 3
The Biology of Mountain Plants....... 5
Immigration and Distribution.......... 8

Plant Communities................. 14
Description of Species............... 20
Index............................ 170
Glossary......................... 173

# PREFACE TO THE FOURTH EDITION

In 1952 the first Norwegian edition of this flora was published. Since then several Norwegian, Swedish and English editions, and even a Finnish one, have been issued.

The new edition, simultaneously published in Norwegian, Swedish and English, is revised and extended. The number of species illustrated have increased from 150 to 164 in order to meet the wishes to include some forest species,

e.g. Red Campion *(Melandrium rubrum)* and Wood Cranesbill *(Geranium sylvaticum)* which are commonly met with in sub-alpine birch forests as well as in the low-alpine belt.

As in previous editions a number of related species are mentioned in the text. The information of distribution and altitude is brought up to date.

Trondheim — Oslo, May 1978.

*Olav Gjærevoll*    *Dagny Tande Lid*

*Reidar Jørgensen*

# MOUNTAINS AND MOUNTAIN FLOWERS

*Mountains* – the very word sounds tempting and like a promise. The word flowers also has beautiful associations and calls forth what is brightest and best in our minds. It is no wonder, therefore, that so many of us who walk about the mountains have formed a friendship for life with the mountain flowers. It is not only their beauty, their lovely colours and forms, their grace, that make us so fond of them. Their brave struggle for life in rather unkind environments increases our sympathy and admiration for them.

In our flora this «alpine family» does not have many members in comparison with other plant groups: on a rough calculation about 250. However, there are so many interesting points about the members of this «family» that one feels tempted to call them the *aristocrats* of our flora.

What quite immediately arrests our attention is their lovely colours. Of course, we know richly coloured flowers from the lowlands, too, but we still get the impression that the alpine flowers surpass all when it comes to pure and fresh colours and a profusion of delicate shades. It may take a little longer before we become alive to their beauty of form. Most conspicuous is the corolla, a strictly regular star being the commonest shape, the petals either pointed, rounded, or square-cut. Very attractive, too, are the many graceful and shapely bells. When you get to know alpine plants more closely, you discover that, in many of them, the *leaves,* too, are well worth observing both for their colour and for their form. With many alpine plants, indeed, it is their graceful *form* and their elegant carriage that, above all, catch our eye. And the mountain wanderer whose sense of smell is as it should be, may, on encountering many of his friends among mountain flowers, rejoice at the fine and characteristic fragrance which — together with the smell of juniper, heather and dwarf birch — helps to intensify his awareness of being in mountain country.

There is a good deal about the look of the

mountain flowers which rouses our interest and excites our desire to get to know them more closely. And our interest grows as we learn a little about why they can thrive in these hard environments, where the summer is both short and cold. Gradually, too, we come to realize the importance of the soil for the individual species, the conditions of distribution, the plant communities, the height-limits of growth, and many, many other things. Then we shall also discover that it is not, indeed, the most conspicuous and beautiful flowers that are really the most interesting.

# THE BIOLOGY OF MOUNTAIN PLANTS

When we think of the care and zeal we display to make the flowers in our gardens thrive, it is hard to understand how plants with beautiful flowers can grow under the conditions met with in the high mountains. We manure, water, protect against frost, weed — and our garden plants have the whole of summer from the end of April to October at their disposal. But how about the mountain plants? Scanty, stony and gravelly soil, extreme scarcity of water for many plants, an average temperature in summer which for the highest-growing, approaches 0°C (32°F), while, for many, the snow reduces summer to one month only!

That, under such conditions, plants can produce flower and fruit, or in some other way provide for the continued existence of their species, can be explained only by way of an almost complete adaption of structure to environment. Let us, therefore, look a little more closely at some of the characteristic features that mountain plants have in common, and the connexion that may be demonstrated between the structure of a plant and its conditions of growth.

Even though we may recall many warm days in the mountains, the average temperature of the summer months is rather low, lower than most people realize. Just look at the figures from Fanaråken in the Jotunheimen Mountains, 2100 metres (7000′) above sealevel:

| | |
|---|---|
| May | ÷ 4,5°C |
| June | ÷ 0,1°C |
| July | + 2,6°C |
| August | + 2,1°C |
| September | ÷ 1,4°C |

It is suprising, too, that the plants manage to keep alive during winter, particularly on the windswept, snowless mountain ridges. A feature which plants in mountain regions have in common with those of the arctic is their amazing capacity to endure the low winter temperatures.

The meagre supply of warmth is the primary reason why plants with a woody stem are so sparingly represented among the mountain plants. The «ripening» of the wood requires more heat than the mountains regions can offer. That is why spruce, pine, birch, juniper, and willows disappear as we climb higher and higher, and although certain woody heather-like species persist to astonishing altitudes, they make up a very small fraction of the plants that «populate» the highest regions.

We find many characteristic structural traits of mountain plants which must be regarded as having some connexion with the scanty amounts of heat at their disposal. The temperature is highest, of course, just above the ground, and there is a marked tendency among mountain plants to keep close to the ground. We find many with creeping stems and a marked dwarfness of growth. Experiments in the Alps have shown that lowland species cultivated in higher regions develop shorter stems and smaller leaves. A contributory cause of this dwarfing is the great light intensity in mountain regions. Plants forming rosettes, tufts and carpets are all characteristic of mountain vegetation. By means of this «crowding together» they shelter and warm each other. Their ability to stand frost, even in summer, is unique. Even in the midst of the

flowering season they can stand days with snow and nights of frost. You can see the Glacier Buttercup bore its way up through layers of snow and ice.

Though many mountain plants have a sufficient water supply, many of them have to make shift with a bare minimum. On wind-swept ridges the evaporation is even particularly great. It is obvious that in such places the plants by means of an exceptionally welldeveloped root system make the utmost use of the moisture at hand. The rootlets are many and long, and the water absorbed is utilized with the greatest care. The slits are protected in various ways, by means of hairiness or by the edges of the leaves being curved inwards, whereby the evaporation is reduced to a minimum.

The plants that can stand life in high mountain regions might with good reason be called «plants of the short summer». Many of them have a pitifully short time at their disposal for the production of stem, leaf, flower and fruit. In many places the snow lies until well into July, and as early as August it may be back again. This means an intense life during a few hectic summer weeks, and that so many of them manage to produce their fruits in less than a month is due to the most perfect adaption to the conditions of life. Growth is swift and intense. Only a few days after the snow has melted the plant can be seen with green stems and leaves. Specimens of Snow Buttercup (No. 76) in full bloom have been observed five days after the snow was gone, and only 17 days later the plant was standing there with fully ripe seeds. There is every reason to wonder how a thing like this can come to pass. The explanation is to be found in a laborious and patient preparation stretching over years and years. Let us for instance look at the developement of the Glacier Buttercup (No. 72) from the time of its germination, when it embarks on life, until many years later its climax is reached: flowering and seed-setting. In the first summer only the seedleaves are developed; they are green and photosynthetic. The rootlets grow a little, and leaf-buds are laid down for the next summer. In the second summer two or three small leaves are brought out which, by their photosynthetic activities during the summer, fortify the root system. New leafbuds are formed for the next summer. In this way life goes on for several summers, the leaves getting ever larger and the leaf-rosette ever stronger. At last the plant has grown sufficiently to develop all the vital parts of which a flower consists, and when the snow disappears the following summer, everything is well prepared for a speedy flowering.

Even though mountain plants, in general, are unequalled in their capacity to produce mature seeds in record time, yet conditions can sometimes be such that they have to give in. All the same, there are other possibilities of reproduction, viz. *vegetatively*. By means of bulbils, runners (stolons) striking roots, and by means of underground stems, they still manage to fullfil their mission in life: to ensure the survival of their species.

# IMMIGRATION AND DISTRIBUTION

For a long time it has been a controversial issue *when* and *from where* the mountain plants have migrated to Scandinavia. It is not easy to elucidate this obscure point, for the plants took possession of the country long before man could do so. Scandinavia has gone through several Ice Ages. We know that during the last of them the great ice-sheet reached as far south as Northern Germany. About 15.000 years ago a climatic change occurred, and the ice began to recede from south, east and west. Close to the ice-margin in Northern Germany and in Russia there existed some hardy plants. As the ice receded these plants were able to follow behind, taking posession

of the new soil. In this way. it was thought, they also reached the mountain regions of Scandinavia.

As it grew warmer, these hardy pioneers were ousted from the lowlands by the forest and by species requiring higher temperatures, and that is how they came to be mountain plants. Now, this sounds very clear and simple. The theory was corroborated by the fact that in quite a few places in Southern Sweden remnants were found of a hardy tundra flora at the bottom of bogs. There were dwarf birch, bearberry, mountain avens, and various willow species, all of them species which are now only exceptionally found outside the mountain region. Besides, there are today a few isolated occurrences of mountain plants in Southern Sweden, e.g. Alpine Butterwort (No. 146) in Gotland, whereas it is otherwise met with only from Härjedalen northwards. These occurrences can only be explained as remnants of the flora which followed close behind the ice. When, in addition to this, we consider the fact that the Scandinavian and Central European mountains have many species in common, it would seem reasonable to presume that our entire mountain flora migrated from the south and east after the last Ice Age.

If we look into the total distribution of our mountain plants, we shall find that many of them have a circumpolar distribution, i.a. they are found more or less continuously in the northern regions of Europe, Asia and America. Numbers of them also occur in the mountains of Central Europe. Some species are confined to the Northern and Central European mountains. This applies to the False Orchid (No. 39). Others may also occur in Asia, e.g. the above-mentioned Alpine Butterwort. Further, we have some species which, apart from Scandinavia, are found also in the Arctic areas of the West, in Greenland, North America and the eastern parts of Siberia. It is in particular this group which brought the theory of the migration of the mountain plants from the south and east up for discussion. The plants belonging to this group are called *West-Arctic*. They cannot possibly have migrated from the south and east, and a migration in modern times, e.g. from Greenland, is out of the questions. A single explanation then remains, namely that the plants must have been in this country during the Ice Age. The great ice-sheet cannot have covered the whole country; there must have been ice-free areas in several places along our coast, and here the plants were able to «hibernate».

Considerations of space forbid us to deal with the latter development of botanical opinion. The view that has come to be endorsed by an ever growing number of botanists is that a substantial part of our mountain flora must have survived the last Ice Age on or near the coast. This is what is known as the hibernation theory. In Norrland (in Sweden) no remnants of any hardy flora have been found in the bottom layers of bogs, such as were found in Southern Sweden. The stream of mi-

9

gration from the south does not seem to have reached to the mountains because it was overtaken by the advancing forest which took possession of the new areas and thus barred the way to the mountain plants.

We know now that Jämtland and Härjedalen (both in Western Sweden) became ice-free from the west. While there was still some ice left in the south and east, fossil finds from this period show that mountain plants had settled there. They must have come from the west, from the Ice Age refuges.

In support of the hibernation theory, reference may be made to Greenland which is in an Ice Age at the present times with an enormous ice-sheet covering the greater part of the country, but with some large ice-free coastal areas where a number of plants grow. In the heart of the glacier, peaks towering above the ice can also boast a considerable number of plants. For such ice-free areas in the middle of a glacier we use the Eskimo word *nunataks*.

It would not seem unreasonable to assume that, to some extent, the situation was the same in Scandinavia during the last Ice Age as it is in Greenland today. There are geological proofs that the outermost islands in Lofoten,

Værøy and Røst, were not glaciated. The biological proof in support of the hibernation theory is constantly being added to. The migration problem itself has thus been thrust further back in time but has not, of course, become less complicated through that. The fact remains, however, that there is a biological relationship between Scandinavia and the Arctic regions in the west, and that this must date from long ago. We know little of how this relationship came about, but possibly there was once a land-connection between Scandinavia and Greenland.

When we study the distribution of mountain plants in Scandinavia, many interesting things come to light. Individual species show great dissimilarities with regard to distribution. Climate and soil play their part, but in many cases it is impossible to explain the distribution of a plant solely on the basis of climatic or geological conditions. Most of our c. 250 mountain plants are found all along the Scandinavian mountain range from Ryfylke to the Varanger peninsula. By way of examples of this type of distribution, we may mention Loiseleuria, Black Bearberry, and Roseroot.

The other species, in a peculiar way, form two clearly distinct areas. One is in Southern Norway, stretching from Jotunheimen across Dovre to Trollheimen. The other area is larger. It begins a little south of the Arctic Circle and comprises part of the county of Nordland and the Swedish Lapland, besides Troms and Western Finnmark.. In these two areas we find by far the greater part of our rare mountain species. Two degrees of latitude separate these areas, and the mountains in between have few botanical pecularities to offer.

Some species, about 30, are found in both areas. These are called *bicentric*. To this type belongs e.g. Arctic Harebell (No. 148); see fig. 1.

A smaller number of species occur only in the southern area; they are called *southern unicentric*. An excellent instance is afforded by the Norwegian Wormwood (No. 157); see fig. 2.

About 35 species grow in the northern area only; they are known as *northern unicentric*. Hairy Lousewort (No. 141) may be taken as a representative of this type of distribution; see fig. 3.

By way of a connecting link between the species distributed all along the mountain range and the distinctly bicentric ones, there are some species which have their principal distribution in the two above-mentioned areas, but which also occur here and there in the area in between. These are generally said to be vaguely bisentric.

The explanation of the distribution of the centric species must be an historical one. There must have been in Norway two main areas of ice-free refuges, one in Møre-Romsdal, and a larger one in Northern Norway. From these refuges the plants then commenced their migrations. Some succeeded in spreading all along the range of mountains, others have merely come part of the way. The present distribution of the plants thus helps to show where the ice-free areas might have been. It is difficult to make out whether the hibernation has taken place only on the coast or on nunataks as well, but once you presuppose that there have been ice-free coastal refuges, e.g. at Møre, you can hardly exclude nunataks in the high mountains inland.

It is worth observing that the majority of the important West-Arctic species are centric.

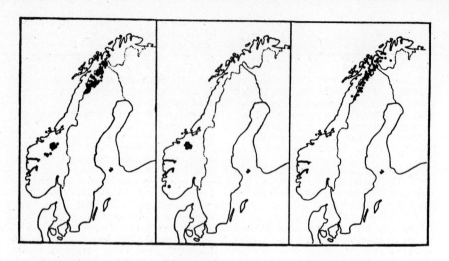

Fig. 1.
Distribution of a
bicentric species, Arctic
Harebell,
in Scandinavia.

Fig. 2.
Distribution of a southern
unicentric species,
Norwegian Wormwood,
in Scandinavia.

Fig. 3.
Distribution of a northern
unicentric species,
Hairy Lousewort,
in Scandinavia.

The same applies to some species which are known only from the mountains of Scandinavia. Species whose total distribution is considerably restricted, are called endemics. The Dovre Dandelion (*Taraxacum dovrense)* is endemic in the southern area. The endemic species are important as evidence for the hibernation theory.

# PLANT COMMUNITIES

It is when we take leave of the coniferous forest and enter the birch wood that we encounter the mountain for the first time. It is not the tall and straightgrained birches of the lowlands that we meet, but stunted, crooked and twisted little trees. Because of the low temperature and the short summer the mountain birch grows very slowly. That is what makes the wood so hard, and that is also the reason why it makes such excellent firewood. The great masses of snow and the high winds cause the crooked, twisted trunks and branches.

The width of this birch belt varies, but we find it in practically all mountains as a «buffer», between the coniferous forest and the upper treeless zones. The upper limit of the birch-belt can be followed as a zig-zag line across the mountain side. In valleys it is drawn upwards, whereas screes and bogs force it downwards.

In the birch wood we come across many *plant communities*. We need not study the plants very closely before we discover that some species thrive extremely well together — they form communities. The causes of this and of the distribution of the plants in general are primarily a difference in the thickness of the snow cover, variations in the calcareousness of the soil, water supply, and altitude. On the birch-wood hillside we may for instance chance upon a plant community of a fantastic luxuriance. We find a large number of stately species, a good many of them as much as 2 m. high, e.g. Monkshood, Blue Sow-thistle, Melancholy Thistle, White Buttercup, Archangelica, quite a few species of grass, and many exuberant ferns. We are familiar with a number of these from the lowlands, and many of them may be found well above the birch line when the conditions are favourable, e.g. in south-facing hills and scree slopes. It is obvious that the cause of this luxuriant vegetation is a rich humus and an ample supply of water.

The other extreme is found where the soil is dry and poor. Here the birch wood becomes sparse, and the ground between the trees is mostly occupied by lichens, especially reindeer lichen. Between these two extremes we find transitional stages. As a rule they are monotonous communities, poor in species, bilberry and some other heath species predominating, while Dwarf Cornel, Cow-wheats, Golden-rod and a few other species are the only ones that provide a relief for this monotony.

When, on our way up, we take leave of the last birch, we have reached the *treeless zone*. It is in this region that we find the habitat of the genuine mountain plants, and from the birch line up to the highest peak there are a great many things of interest to the mountain walker. As is to be expected, the number of species decreases as you mount higher. Sometimes this decrease is quite gradual; more often, however, it is rather irregular — according to the geological conditions. On steep, southfacing mountains where rocks, crags, clefts and shelves afford shelter, we often find a vegetation so rich in species and so interesting that it has all a botanist can ever wish for. But once you get over the ridge and on to the more gently sloping plateau where screes and frost-broken rocks dominate the landscape, the number of species again drops to a minimum.

Botanists have found it natural to divide the tree-less zone into three belts, the *low-alpine belt* from where the birch wood peters out and as far up as the bilberries go. The *middle-alpine belt* has an upper limit which is very much of a geological nature in that the areas dominated by snow, ice, scree and rocks are reckoned as belonging to the *high-alpine belt*.

*The low-alpine belt.*

The plant communities most easily distinguished are the bogs. Bogs are not the kind of ground that the mountain walker loves best, but the vegetation is sometimes so interesting that it makes up for a good deal. The bogs built up by bog-mosses *(Sphagnum)*, are poor in species. This also applies to fens on non-calcareous soil. Dominant species are e.g. Mud Sedge and Bog Sedge. Particularly conspicuous are the cotton grass communities, which can be dominated both by Common Cotton-grass and by Arctic Cotton-grass. The latter sometimes occurs in enormous numbers on sandy soil near lakes and rivers and in flat high-alpine bogs. On calcarous soil the pictures

15

is quite a different one; this is especially true of irrigated sloping fens. First of all we notice Yellow Mountain-Saxifrage and Dark-brown Sedge. Other species forming communities are Russet Sedge, Small-spiked Sedge and Tufted Clubrush, the last of which also occurs on soil poor in lime. Calcareous fens are among the communities that are the richest in species. In the bottom layer the brown mosses predominate.

Let us look a little more closely at the importance of *snow* as far as the plants are concerned. Everyone who has walked in the mountains in winter is familar with the fact that, because of the wind, the snow is unevenly distributed over the ground. The snow is blown away from ridges and peaks, and accumulates in hollows and depressions. The distribution of snowless ridges and snowdrifts is the same from year to year. This fact is clearly reflected in the vegetation, so clearly, indeed, that civil engineers who are staking out the line of a projected road in the mountains, consult the botanist. The road should be laid where the snow cover is thinnest, and such areas the botanist is able to point out in summer on the basis of the vegetation.

To get a picture of the significance of the snow cover, we may look at a non-calcareous morainic ridge. On the exposed ridge we find a community of xerophilous plants. In winter they are severely exposed to drought because of the wind, and in summer the only supply of water is in the form of rain. On the most windswept ridges the soil or gravel is often bare, and the hardiest vegetation consists of small brown and black crustaceous and foliaceous lichens, which are strong enough to lie bare of snow all through the winter. Otherwise, the ridges afford a very characteristic community which, primarily, consists of Loiseleuria, Crowberry, Black Bearberry, Lapland Diapensia and Cranberry. Where the snow-cover is somewhat better in winter, a zone will be found where dwarf birch, Bog Whortleberry, and Blue Mountain-heath are extremely conspicuous. A little distance further down the slope where the snow cover is solid but the exposure fairly early, we get a very clearly demarcated community in which the Bilberry is particularly dominant. Both the upper boundary on the heath communities and the lower one on the snow beds are very distinct.

The *snow bed communities* open with a

grass zone which is very conspicuous in the landscape because of its colour. Important species are Wavy-Hair-grass, Sweet Vernal-grass, and Mat-grass, the last-mentioned especially in Western Norway. If the ground is very moist, Buttercup, Two-flowered Violet and Dandelion will be in evidence. On stony ground the stout fern, Alpine Lady-fern *(Athyrium distentifolium)*, will predominate.

When the snow is lying so long that the species mentioned above seem to have very little vitality left, dominance is taken over by the Least Willow. Over great areas it may be the only vascular plant. The leaves are pressed down against a more or less compact carpet of hardy snow-bed mosses. It is often found in company with Dwarf Cudweed, and Mossy Mountain-heather. With even later exposure the vascular plants disappear completely, and gray and dark mosses — together with the orange lichen *Solorina crocea* — command the ground between them. Eventually, these outposts of life on the border of bare gravel and ice are also forced to capitulate.

If we take a corresponding section on calcareous soil, we get an entirely different picture. On the ridges the Mountain Avens must be said to be the most characteristic plant. This community has incomparably more numerous species than are found on soil poor in lime. Here we find many of the most interesting species of all, such as Arctic Harebell, Whitlow-grasses, Snow Cinquefoil, Lapland Rhododendron, Norwegian Wormwood in the south, and Alpine Arnica in the north. In many places the Bellard's Kobresia plays an important part. The Mountain Avens heaths are the most gorgeous plant communities in the mountains. They offer a variegated play of colours: white, blue, yellow, violet. All the milk-vetch species grow here, with Scandinavian Primrose, Moss Campion, and several orchids, such as False Orchid and Small White Orchid.

Characteristic of the grass zone in snow beds is the Alpine Poa. The Least Willow communities are replaced by the Polar Willow communities. On moist ground you will find a colourful community with Purple Saxifrage, Drooping Saxifrage, Mountain Sorrel, Alpine Rockcress, Alpine Willowherb, Sandworts and Chickweeds, Alpine Whitlow-grass and Pigmy Buttercup.

In the lower part of the tree-less mountain we may come across lovely, luxuriant communities which go by the name *meadows*. Here we particularly find species requiring a good deal of moisture. They oust the heather species and other plants of exposed ridges. Especially in the north the Globe Flower is in evidence, but other representatives of the tall herbs that we found on the birch hillside are to be seen here, too. Further, we may mention Viviparous Knotweed, Alpine Cinquefoil, Common Buttercup, Alpine Saussurea, Alpine Bartsia and Alpine Poa. Possibly we may be justified in regarding some of the plants that we know from the lowlands and which we find in these meadows as remnants of a flora from the time when the timber line went higher than it does today.

### The middle-alpine belt.

In this belt we find largely the same species and many of the same plant communities that were mentioned from the low-alpine belt, but the vegetation is more sparse. The bilberry has disappeared and so have dwarf birch and willow thickets. Snow bed communities cover very large areas. It is here that the Glacier Buttercup is met with, forming a bright spot in this desolate landscape. In its company it has i.a. Northern Woodrush, Alpine Cress, and Least Willow. On gravel which is quite soaked with water from the melting snow, the tiny little Snowgrass (*Phippsia algida*) may be found.

Otherwise grass and sedge communities are found with species such as Three-leaved Rush, Sheep's Fescue, and Stiff Sedge.

### The high-alpine belt.

Here we no longer find any continous vegetation of heath or grass species. The plants grow so sparsely that we can no longer speak of plant communities. One should realize, however, that a good many more species are found growing here than most people would expect. It may seem surprising to many that in Jotunheimen close upon 40 different flowering plants have been found at an altitude of more than 2.000 m. At these altitudes the specimens are often small and fairly well hidden from the eye.

In conclusion, we would mention one of the communities that are often most rewarding for botanists. We are thinking of communities indigenous to *scree slopes* where the soil is calcareous and rich in loose schists. Such south-facing scree slopes are the habitats of many of the rarest species of our flora. Arctic poppies, Rock Speedwell, and Norwegian Sandwort are typical scree-slope plants, and so are also Northern Rock-cress, Smoothing Braya and Ascending Saxifrage.

## 1. Fir Clubmoss

### *Lycopodium selago* L.

5—12 cm. Stems forked, with lanceolate, acute leaves in 8 rows. Yellow sporangia in the axils of the upper leaves. In the axils of some of the uppermost leaves bulbils which break off when the leaves are touched. Poisonous. A decoction of the plant has been used against lise on people and animals.

In lowland areas in coniferous forests; on the mountains especially in heaths and on tops; snow beds. Throughout Scandinavia, very common. Jotunheimen Mts 1940 m. Troms 1636 m.

Europe, Greenland, N. and S. America, some islands in the southern Atlantic ocean, N. and C. Asia, Tasmania, New Zealand.

## 2. Alpine Clubmoss

### *Lycopodium alpinum* L.

Stems prostrate, 15—50 cm., branches forked and densely tufted. Leaves 4-ranked on the branches. Sporangia in cones sessile at the ends of branches.

In bilberry heaths and early exposed snow beds, frequently very abundant, particularly on acid soils. Throughout the Scandinavian mountain range, very common. Mt Galdhøpiggen 1625 m. Troms 1060 m.

Europe, Greenland, America, Asia Minor, N. Asia.

In the mountains also Stag's-Horn Moss *(L. clavatum)* and Interrupted Clubmoss *(L. annotinum)* occur. The leaves of the former end in a white flexuous hair-point, whereas in the latter they end in a short stiff point.

Notes:

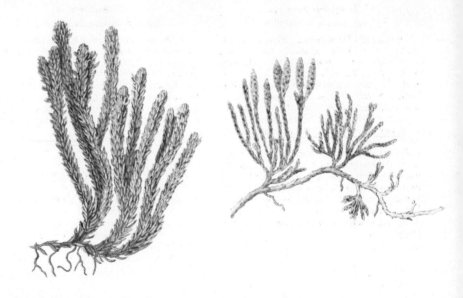

1                                    2

### 3. Sedge-like Horsetail

*Equisetum scirpoides* Rich.

5—20 cm. Decumbent, densely tufted, stems stiff, jointed, persisting through the winter. At every node a sheath ending in 3—4 teeth. Spikes terminal.

Wet, sandy soil, snow beds, fens and river bars, preferably on base-rich soils. Hallingdal—Varanger, fairly rare. Missing in W. Norway. Dovre 1350 m. Troms 1100 m.

N. Europe (not in the British Isles), Greenland, N.America, N.Asia.

The related species Variegated Horsetail *(E. variegatum)* is bigger and stiffer, usually unbranched or less branched, number of teeth 6—12. Moist, base-rich soils. Setesdal —Varanger, fairly rare. S. Norway 1400 m. Troms 1100 m. Distribution about the same as for *Equisetum scirpoides,* but also in the British Isles.

### 4. Moonwort

*Botrychium lunaria* (L.) Sw.

5—20 cm. Underground rhizome with a solitary leaf divided into a sterile pinnate blade and a fertile branched spike. The pinnae are usually crescent-shaped and entire.

Grassland throughout Scandinavia, common. Jotunheimen Mts 1700. Troms 885 m.

Europe, Greenland, N.America, Patagonia, Asia, Australia, New Zealand, N. and S. Africa.

### 5. Northern Grape-fern

*Botrychium boreale* Milde

5—12 cm. Differs from *B. lunaria* by having a more triangular blade and lobed pinnae.

Grassland throughout the mountains on calcareous soils. Hallingdal—Varanger, rare, Jotunheimen Mts 1600 m. Troms 1300 m.

N.Europe, Greenland, N. America. Siberia.

3                                    4                        5

## 6. Parsley Fern

*Cryptogramma crispa* (L.) R.Br.

15—25 cm. Separate fertile leaves, with stalks longer than those of sterile leaves. Sterile leaves pinnate, segments of pinnae broad and toothed. Fertile leaves pinnate, segments linear, margins of segments recurved, covering the sori. The species is considered poisonous, especially to horses.

Screes (esp. with a long-lasting snow cover) on acid soils, commonly associated with Alpine Lady-fern *(Athyrium distentifolium).* In W. and N. Norway down to sea level. Throughout the mountains, fairly common. Jotunheimen 1550 m. Troms 875 m.

Europe, Asia Minor, Afganistan, W. Siberia.

Notes:

## 7. Green Spleenwort

*Asplenium viride* Huds.

5—15 cm. Creeping rhizome, leaves densely tufted, usually persistent, not coriaceous. Stalks brownish near the base, green above, rhachis green. Sori linear near the midrib of the pinnae.

Crevices of calcareous rocks and olivine. Throughout the mountains, but rare in the eastern and northernmost parts. Frequently met with also in the lowlands. Jotunheimen 1700 m. Troms 1020 m.

Europe, Greenland, N.America, N. and C. Asia, Atlas.

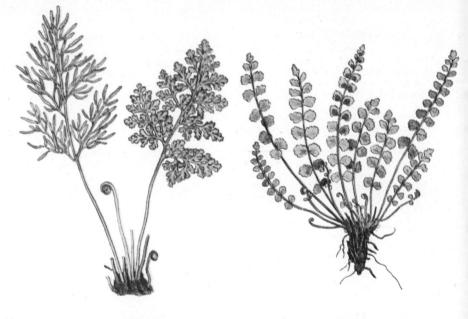

6                                    7

## 8. Alpine Woodsia

*Woodsia alpina* (Bolt.) Gray

5—10 cm. Rhizome short and branched, leaves tufted. At the middle of the stalk there is a joint. Sori circular (orbicular).

Rock crevices on base-rich soils, not common. Also in the lowlands. Dovre 1400 m.
Europe, Greenland, N. America, Siberia.

Smooth Woodsia *(W. glabella)* is northern unicentric in Scandinavia. Grows in rock crevices, on exposed ridges and heaths from Saltdal and Pite Lappmark to the Varanger Peninsula. Differs from Alpine Woodsia by lacking scales on the stalks above the joint. Troms 1050 m.

Europe, Greenland, N.America, Asia.


Notes:

## 9. Holly Fern

*Polystichum lonchitis* (L.) Roth

20—50 cm. Rhizome short and stout. Leaves persistent, coriaceous, deep green above, lobes of the pinnae serrate with spine-pointed teeth. Sori circular, regularly arranged in a row on each side of the midrib of the pinnae.

Crevices and screes in the birch region and above the timber line, in some places also in the lowland, preferably on base-rich soils. Throughout the mountains, but rare in the northeastern parts. — Jotunheimen 1500 m. Troms 800 m.

Europe, Greenland, N.America, Asia.

8            9

## 10. Sweet Vernal-grass

*Anthoxanthum odoratum* L.

10—20 cm. July—Aug. In small tufts. Leaves somewhat scabrous, sheaths usually pubescent. When dry the Sweet Vernal-grass has a pleasant smell of coumarin («New-Moonhay»). The species shows a considerable variation. the mountain form has been described as a species of its own, *A. alpinum*. The chromosome number is 2n = 10, whereas the main lowland form has 2n = 20. The awn is longer in the mountain form and the glumes are glabrous.

One of the most common grasses of heaths and meadows throughout Scandinavia, Jotunheimen 2130 m. Troms 1070 m.

Europe, N. Africa, Asia, introduced in America and Australia. *A alpinum:* N. Europe, Greenland, Siberia.

## 11. Alpine Timothy

*Phleum commutatum* Gaud.

15—25 cm. July—Aug. Previously called *P. alpinum,* but this species is restricted to Central and S. Europe. Differs from Timothy *(P. pratense)* as follows: Culm shorter, upper sheaths strongly inflated, panicle shorter, more ovoid and darker, awn longer.

Birch forests, willow thickets, mountain farms, grassland, partly in moist and late exposed snow beds. Throughout the mountains, common, descending to the lowland, Jotunheimen 1800 m. Troms 1040 m.

Europe, Greenland, N. America, Andes of S. America, Asia.

10                                   11

## 12 Alpine Hair-grass
### *Deschampsia alpina* (L.) R. et Sch.

20—40 cm. Tufted, leaves scabrous. Viviparous, no seeds are produced, the upper part of the spikelets develops into a bulbil which falls off and strikes root.

Moist gravel and sand by creeks and lakes, flushed snow beds. Setesdal — Varanger, common. Jotunheimen 2230 m. Troms 1260 m.

British Isles, Scandinavia, Iceland, Greenland, Arctic Russia and Siberia.

Wavy Hair-grass (*D. flexuosa*). Leaves narrow, inrolled, panicle narrow, lax, branches flexuous. Spikelets reddish or purplish. Meadows, snow beds. Very common. Jotunheimen 1900 m. Troms 1200 m.

Mountain Hair-grass *(Vahlodea atropurpurea)* has flat, short leaves. Panicle lax, spikelets purplish-brownish. Moist places, willow thickets, snow beds. Throughout the mountains, rare in the southern part. Hardangervidda 1600 m. Troms 800 m. West-arctic.

## 13. Spiked Trisetum
### *Trisetum spicatum* (L.) Richt.

10—25 cm. July—Aug. Loosely tufted. Culm and leaves pubescent. Lemma with a long-exserted awn.

Meadows, heath and ledges, preferably on base-rich soils. Hardangervidda—Varanger, fairly common. Jotunheimen 2280 m. Troms 1450 m.

Europe, Greenland, N. America. Haiti, S. America, Asia, Tasmania.

## 14. Violet Wheat-grass
### *Roegneria borealis* (Turcz.) Nevski

20—40 cm. July—Aug. Culms solitary or tufted, stiff. Screes, crevices and exposed ridges on base-rich soils. Setesdal—Varanger, rare. Finse 1450 m. Troms 1030 m. Arctic parts of Europe, America and Asia.

*R. mutabilis* is taller (1 m), spikelets larger, dark purplish. Birch forests, willow thickets and luxuriant meadows. North-eastern species. Lule Lappmark—Varanger, rare.

12          13          14

## 15. Alpine Poa

*Poa alpina* L.

15—30 cm. Easily recognized by its light-coloured persistent, fibrous remains of basal leaves and sheaths. At high altitudes viviparous.

Both the normal and the viviparous form common throughout the mountains, the normal one also in the lowlands. Often predominating in meadows with a long-lasting snow-cover. Preferably on base-rich soils. Jotunheimen 2000 m. (f. *vivipara* 2140 m). Troms 1450 m.

Europe, Greenland, N. America, N. Asia, Caucasus.

Further viviparous species: *P. jemtlandica.* Tufts loose, culms shorter and more slender than with *P. alpina,* panicle wine-red. Ryfylke—Åsele Lappmark.

*P. herjedalica.* Culms tall, the sheaths at the base not as prominent as in *P. alpina.* Throughout the mountains.

*P. stricta.* Tufted, stoloniferous. Endemic in Central Norway.

## 16. Snow Grass

*Phippsia algida* (Sol.) R. Br.

5 cm, densely tufted. Leaves hooded. Panicle narrow, greenish-yellow. Spikelets 1-flowered, with tiny, scaly glumes. Lemma faintly pubescent in the lower part. Anthers 2. Snow beds at high altitudes irrigated during the whole summer. Suldal and Bykle—Haltdalen. Hattfjelldal—Finnmark. Dovre 1680 m. Troms 1324 m.

Arctic parts of Europe, Asia and N. America.

*P. concinna* occurs in a few localities at Dovre. Panicle violet with divergent branches. Lemma white-haired in the lower half. Anther 1. Usually in the same kind of localities as *P. algida,* but may also occur in drier snow beds.

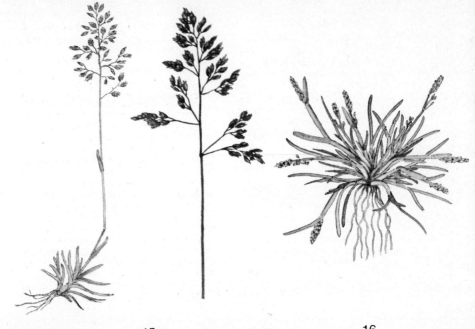

15

16

### 17. Arctic Cotton-grass
#### *Eriophorum scheuchzeri* Hoppe

10—30 cm. Creeping rhizome, stems solitary. «Cotton» bristles shiny white. Frequently in mass vegetation in fens and wet sandy places by creeks and lakes. Common throughout the mountains. Jotunheimen 1800 m. Troms 1080 m. Europe (not British Isles), Greenland, Arctic America, Arctic Siberia.

Hare's tail *(E. vaginatum)* differs as follows: Stems densely tufted, sheaths strongly inflated. Peat bogs. Common throughout Scandinavia. Jotunheimen 1710 m. Troms 840 m.

Close-sheated Cotton-grass *(E. brachyantherum)*: Stems loosely tufted, sheaths not inflated, bristles yellowish. Valdres—Varanger, rare. Troms 925 m.

### 18. Common Cotton-grass
#### *Eriophorum angustifolium* Honck.

50 cm. Culms from creeping rhizome. Leaves dark green, channelled, ending in a long tip. Peduncles smooth, Spikelets broad at the base. Bogs and fens all over Scandinavia. Jotunheimen 1700 m. Troms 1115 m.

Europe, Asia, N. America.

### 19. Arctic Kobresia
#### *Kobresia simpliciuscula* (Wg.) Mack.

10—30 cm. July—Aug. Densely tufted with remains of previous year's leaves at the base. Spikes male at top, female below. Differs from sedge *(Carex)* as follows: The inner glume does not form a flaskshaped «utricle» around the nut, but only enfolds it.

Moist slopes and fens on base-rich soils. Hardangervidda—Lycksele Lappmark, not common. Hardangervidda 1450 m. A single locality in Finland. Europe, Greenland, N. America, C. Asia.

Bellard's Kobresia *(K. myosuroides)*. Stems tufted, slender but stiff, smooth. 10—20 cm. Spike single, narrow. Dry and exposed ridges and heaths on calcareous soils. Hardangervidda—Finnmark, not common. Jotunheimen 1900 m. Troms 1030 m.

17                   18                  19

## 20. Small-spiked Sedge

### *Carex microglochin* Wg.

5—15 cm. July—Aug. Stems stiff and straight from creeping runners, often in extensive growths. Single spike, male at the top. Fruits at first erect, later deflexed. A bristle from the base of the nut protrudes from the top of the beak.

Fens, gravelly spots, only on calcareous soils, fairly rare. Hardangervidda—Porsanger. Hardangervidda 1450 m. Troms 870 m. Europe, Greenland, N. and S. America, C. Asia.

Rock Sedge *(C. rupestris):* Fruits erect, leaves involute and curled, dry-looking. Ledges, crevices and exposed ridges on base-rich soils. Ryfylke–Varanger, common. Jotunheimen 2100 m. Troms 1380 m.

Notes:

## 21. Capitate Sedge

### *Carex capitata* Sol.

15—30 cm. July. Densely tufted. Single spike, male at the top. Beak of the fruit smooth. Scales shorter than the perigynia. Shallow calcareous fens. Hardangervidda—Sør-Varanger. S. Norway 1400 m. Troms 680 m.

Closely related is Northern Sedge *(C. arctogena)* 10—15 cm. Beak of the fruit serrulate. Scales as long as the perigynia. Bicentric, very rare. Jotunheimen. Hattfjelldal—Varanger. Nard Sedge *(C. nardina).* 3—10 cm. Stems and leaves of the same length, curved, densely tufted. Strongly exposed ridges and heaths on calcareous soils. Northern unicentric. Saltfjell—West-Finnmark, rare. Troms 1240 m. West-arctic.

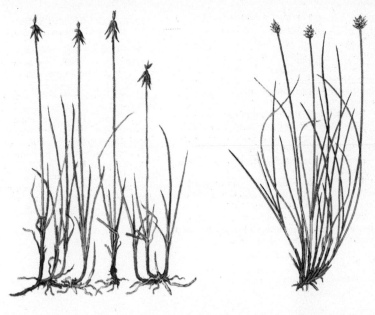

20

21

## 22. Arctic Hare's-foot Sedge

*Carex lachenalii* Schkuhr

10—20 cm. July—Aug. Tufted. Stems stiff, often curved. Male flowers at the base of the upper spikes. Beak smooth. Resembles *Kobresia simpliciuscula* (no. 18), but the latter one has the male flowers at the top of the spikes.

Particularly in snow beds, often in mass vegetation in places irrigated from snow-fields. Setesdal—Varanger, very common. Jotunheimen 1980 m. Troms 1320 m.

Europe, Greenland, N. America, Asia, New Zealand.

Thick-headed Sedge *(C. macloviana)*. Spikes more clustered, broader and darker than with *C. lachenalii*. Margin of the fruit scabrous. Damp meadows. Northern unicentric, Nord-Rana—Tromsøysund. N. Europe, N. America, S. America, NE. Asia.

Notes:

## 23. Stiff Sedge

*Carex bigelowii* Torr.

10—15 cm. July. Rhizome with curved runners. Stems stiff. One male spike at the top. Female glumes blackish with pale green midrib. Stigmas usually 2.

A very common species, occurring in many different kinds of plant communities, heaths, shallow fens, often predominating on early exposed snow beds. Throughout the mountains. Jotunheimen 1950 m. Troms 1360 m.

Europe, Greenland, N. America, N. Asia.

Common Sedge *(C. nigra)*. Stems less stiff, slender, rough above. Wet places, fens. Throughout Scandinavia, very common. Hardangervidda 1250 m. Troms 700 m. Europe, N. America, W. Asia, Australia.

22  23

## 24. Alpine Sedge

*Carex norvegica* Retz.

15—20 cm. July. Stems tufted, erect, rigid, sharp-edged. Terminal spike with male and female flowers, male ones in the upper part. Fruits broad.

Moist grassy places, preferably on base-rich soils. Setesdal—Varanger, common. S. Norway 1600 m. Troms 1055 m.

Europe, Greenland, northeastern parts of N. America, E. Siberia.

Angara Sedge *(C. media)* is closely related. Taller, spikes more clustered. Fruits narrow. Hallingdal—Valdres, rare.

Holostome Sedge *(C. holostoma)* resembles the Alpine Sedge, but has a small male spike between female ones. Damp depressions and on ledges. Northern unicentric. Ofoten—S. Varanger, very rare. Troms 1000 m. West-arctic.

Notes:

## 25. Bicoloured Sedge

*Carex bicolor* All.

5—15 cm. July. Slender, lax stems, downwardly curved and finally lowering the spikes to the ground.

Sandy and gravelly river bars, moist snow beds, solifluction soil, only on base-rich soils. Bicentric, very rare. In South Scandinavia only on river bars in the Dovre Mts area and at the Ljusnan River in Härjedalen. In the north from Saltdal and Lule Lappmark to Porsanger. Dovre 1000 m. Troms 620 m.

Europe, Greenland, arctic N. America, Siberia.

Rufine Sedge *(C. rufina),* 2—5 cm. Tufts flat, spikes dark, resting on the ground. Wet, flat snow beds. Ryfylke—Troms, not common. Hardanger 1600 m. West-arctic.

24                              25

## 26. Black Sedge

### *Carex atrata* L.

15—40 cm. July. Stems usually solitary. Leaves flat and broad. Terminal spike with male flowers at the base only (cf. no. 27). Panicle at first erect, later drooping.

Luxuriant meadows and grassland, also in late exposed places, preferably on base-rich soils. Throughout the mountains, common. Jotunheimen 1920 m. Troms 1100 m.

Europe, Greenland, N. America, Asia.

Short-leafed Sedge *(C. misandra)*. 10—20 cm. Densely tufted. Leaves spreading, twisted. Spikes 3—5, less dark than by *C. atrata,* nodding on slender peduncles. Moist gravelly places. Bicentric, rare. Jotunheimen —Trollheimen. Lule Lappmark—W. Finnmark. Trollheimen 1600 m. Troms 1385 m.

Notes:

## 27. Dark-brown Sedge

### *Carex atrofusca* Schkuhr

15—30 cm. July. Stems stiff, in loose tufts. Terminal spike male (cf. no. 26). Differs from the Short-leafed Sedge (see under no. 26) by having dark-brown glumes, those of the former are hyaline-margined. Female spikes nodding on slender arcuate peduncles. A very beautiful sedge.

Often in mass vegetation on fens and wet hillsides, ledges. Important indicator species of calcareous soils. The localities are always rich in species. Ryfylke—Finnmark, common. Jotunheimen 1880 m. Troms 1040 m.

Europe, Greenland, N. America, Asia.

26               27

## 28. Yellow Sedge
### *Carex flava* L.

15—30 cm. July. Tufts loose. Fruits prominently nerved, beak long and curved. Spikes greenish-yellowish when ripe.

Fens and moist hillsides, preferably on calcareous soils. Throughout Scandinavia, common, also in the lowlands. Hardangervidda 1320 m. Troms 675 m.

Europe, N. America, N. Africa.

## 29. Hair Sedge
### *Carex capillaris* L.

5—20 cm. July. Tufts small and dense. Male spike 1, terminal. Female spikes 2—3, nodding on slender, arcuate peduncles. Tall specimens might be confused with *C. misandra* (cf. no. 26).

Shallow fens, ledges, *Dryas*-heaths, always on base-rich soils. Throughout the mountains, but rare in the southern and western parts. Also in the lowlands. Jotunheimen 1600 m. Troms 960 m.

Europe, Greenland, N. America, N. and E. Asia.

## 30. Russet Sedge
### *Carex saxatilis* L.

15—30 cm. July. Stems rigid, rough above. Leaves rough. Male spike 1, terminal. Female spikes 1—3. Stigmas usually 2. Base-rich fens, often in abundance. Setesdal—Varanger, common. Jotunheimen 1750 m. Troms 1115 m.

N. Europe, Greenland, arctic N. America, Siberia.

Round-fruited Sedge (*C. rotundata*). Stems smooth, stigmas 3. Fens, avoiding base-rich soils. Hardangervidda—Varanger, common. Hardangervidda 1550 m. Troms 760 m.

28          29          30

## 31. Chestnut Rush

*Juncus castaneus* Sm.

15—30 cm. Creeping rhizome with arching stolons. Stems erect, stiff and coarse. Heads 1—3 with 3—6 flowers each. Perianth brownish—black. Capsule much longer than the perianth, chestnut-brown. Wet places, fens, on calcareous soils. Bicentric. Setesdal—Lycksele Lappmark. Kvænangen—Kola. S. Norway 1400 m.

Europe, Greenland, N. America, N. and C. Asia.

## 32. Three-flowered Rush

*Juncus triglumis* L.

8—15 cm. Tufted, leaves subulate. Stems erect, stiff. Usually 3 flowers (2—5). Fens and moist gravel on base-rich soils. Setesdal—Varanger, common. Jotunheimen 1500 m. Troms 1030 m.

Europe, Greenland, N. Americ, Asia.

Two-flowered Rush *(J. biglumis)* is smaller, flowers usually 2, exceeded by the lowest bract. Moist snow beds. Setesdal—Varanger, common. Jotunheimen 1840 m. Troms 1260 m. Europe, N. America, N. Asia.

## 33. Three-leaved Rush

*Juncus trifidus* L.

10—20 cm. Densely tufted. Flowers in small clusters between axils of 2—3 filiform bracts overtopping the inflorescence.

A very abundant species on heaths and ridges, particularly above the bilberry heaths, preferably on hard rocks. Throughout the mountains, common. Jotunheimen 1850 m. Troms 1120 m.

Europe, Greenland, northeastern N. America, Siberia.

31             32             33

## 34. Arctic Rush

*Juncus arcticus* Willd.

20—30 cm. Culms stout in rows from horizontal rootstocks. Cluster of flowers apparently lateral, exceeded by a bract, 3,5 cm, appearing like a continuation of the stem. Wet gravel and shallow fens, preferably on calcareous soils. Setesdal—Varanger, rare. Hardangervidda 1330 m. Troms 580 m.

N. and M. Europe, W. Siberia, Greenland.
*Juncus filiformis* is also met with in the mountains, but is not connected with calcareous soils. Stems filiform and bract about as long as stem.

## 35. Smallflowered Woodrush

*Luzula parviflora* (Ehrh.) Desv.

20—50 cm. Leaves usually glabrous, 1 cm broad. Flowers on long slender arching rays. Bractlets entire-margined and glabrous. Capsule chestnut-brown, acute. Moist places in the uppermost part of the birch forest and in willow thickets, on calcareous soils. Bicentric. Hallingdal—Dovre, Lycksele Lappmark—Varanger. Dovre 1350 m. Troms 1030 m.

Wahlenberg's Woodrush *(L. wahlenbergii)*: 15—25 cm, bractlets lacerate and ciliate. Moist places, snow beds. Härjedalen — Varanger.

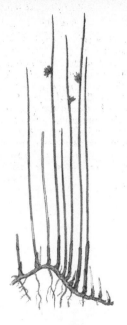

34                                  35

## 36. Curved Woodrush

*Luzula arcuata* Wg.

10—20 cm. Flowers in small clusters on slender branches. Leaves channelled. Dry rocks and mountain tops. Setesdal—Varanger. Dovre 1500 m.

The northern parts of Europe, America and Asia.

Northern Woodrush *(L. confusa)* is closely related. Stem stouter, clusters of flowers more erect. Heaths and ridges, often abundant. Throughout the mountains, common. Jotunheimen 2220 m. Troms 1636 m.

*Luzula frigida.* Leaves flat, pubescent, 3—4 heads on erect rays, one of the rays usually exceeding the other ones. Grassy slopes and meadows.

## 37. Spiked Woodrush

*Luzula spicata* (L.) DC.

10—20 cm. Tufted. Flowers in a dense spike-like drooping cyme. Dry places, heaths and plateaus throughout the mountains, common. Jotunheimen 2220 m. Troms 1350 m.

Europe, Greenland, N. America, Asia.

Arctic Woodrush *(L. arctica).* 10—15 cm. Leaves broader and shorter than in previous species. Flowers in a dense, short and dark capitate inflorescence. Moist solifluction soil and mossy ledges on base-rich soils. Bicentric, very rare. Dovre—Trollheimen. Lule Lappmark—Troms. Dovre 1650 m. Troms 1300 m.

Notes:

36       37

### 38. Scottish Asphodel
*Tofieldia pusilla* (Michx.) Pers.

8—15 cm. July—Aug. Leaves at the base, 2-ranked vertical and equitant (like any *Iris* leaves), sword-like with sharp margins. Flowers in a close spike. Slightly honey-scented.

Fens and different plant communities rich in species on calcareous soils. Throughout the mountains, common, also in the lowlands. Jotunheimen 1700 m. Troms 1040 m.

Europe, Greenland, N. America, very rare in N. Asia.

### 39. False Orchid
*Chamorchis alpina* (L.) Rich.

5—12 cm. July—Aug. Leaves narrow, channelled. The dark, shrunk root-tuber is that of the previous year, the light, fresh one that of the current year. No smell, but nectar is present.

Dry as well as damp *Dryas*-heaths, damp grassy hills, only on calcareous soils. Slightly bicentric. Jotunheimen—Verdal. Åsele Lappmark and Nordland—Varanger. S. Norway 1570 m. Troms 710 m.

Mountains of N. and C. Europe.

### 40. Fragrant Orchid
*Gymnadenia conopsea* (L.) R. Br.

10—40 cm. July—Aug. Spike 6—15 cm. Flowers reddish-lilac, rarely white, strongly fragrant. Spur long, slender and curved. Meadows and grasslands, fens, preferably on calcareous soils, on south-facing slopes sometimes very abundant. Throughout Scandinavia, common. Hardangervidda 1400 m. Troms 590 m.

Europe, W. Asia.

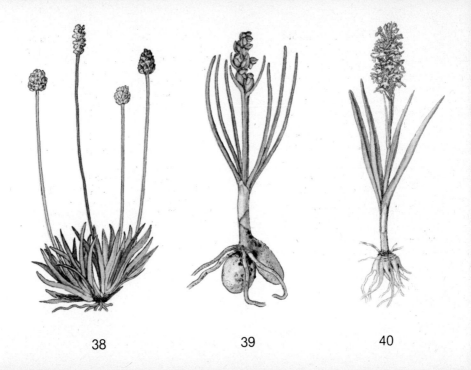

38             39            40

### 41. Small White Orchid

*Leucorchis albida* (L.) E. Mey

10—20 cm. July—Aug. Spike cylindrical, one-sided, flowers vanilla-scented. Root-tubers deeply palmate, resembling a bundle of separate roots. Meadows and grassy hills, *Dryas*-heaths, fens, on calcareous soils. Throughout the mountains, fairly common. Jotunheimen 1800 m. Troms 1000 m.

Europe, Greenland, W. Siberia.

### 42. Scented Nigritella

*Nigritella nigra* (L.) Rchb. fil

10—20 cm. July. Flowers fragrant. Meadows, grassland and fens, preferably on base-rich soils, in the birch forest and above the timber line. Trollheimen 1270 m. Peculiar bicentric distribution: Toten—Velfjord in Nordland, in addition a single locality in Troms (Nordreisa). Eastwards especially abundant in Jämtland (the district flower of Jämtland) down to the Gulf of Bothnia.

Mountains of S. and C. Europe. The Scandinavian population somewhat different from the southern race (apomictic).

### 43. Frog Orchid

*Coeloglossum viride* (L.) Hartm.

10-25 cm. July—Aug. Flowers yellowish-green—brownish. Spur short and ovoid, containing free nectar. Damp grassy hillsides in birch forests, willow thickets and above the timber line. Throughout the mountains, common, also in the lowlands. Jotunheimen 1740 m. Troms 930 m.

Europe, N. America, Asia.

41    42    43

## 44. Reticulate Willow

### *Salix reticulata* L.

July. Dwarf shrub with a branched creeping and rooting stem on and beneath the surface. Leaves 1—3 cm, coriaceous, beneath with silky hairs. Rugose with impressed veins above, reticulate-veined beneath. Shallow fens. *Dryas*-heaths, ridges, ledges, snow beds, often abundant, always on calcareous soils. Ryfylke—Varanger, common. Galdhøpiggen 1940 m. Troms 1267 m.

Europe, N. America, N. Asia. Lacking in Iceland and Greenland.

The willows are diocieous, having the sexes on different plants. They form series of hybrids. The flowers have nectar and they are pollinated by insects.

Notes:

## 45. Least Willow

### *Salix herbacea* L.

July—Aug. Underground branches from a creeping rhizome. Aerial branches very short and prostrate, the leaves usually resting on the ground, crenate-serrate. Capsule glabrous. Late exposed snow beds, often in dense carpets. Abundant also in heaths. Throughout the mountains. very common. Galdhøpiggen 2350 m. Troms 1480 m.

Europe, Greenland, N. America, N. and C. Asia.

Polar Willow *(S. polaris)* resembles very much the Least Willow and is of the same size. Leaves entire-margined, capsule pubescent. Predominating on snow beds on calcareous soils. Hardangervidda—Varanger, not common. Jotunheimen 2000 m. Troms 1450 m.

44
45

## 46. Myrtle Willow

### *Salix myrsinites* L.

June—July. Shrub 30—100 cm. Twigs brown and shining, rugged, with the withered remains of the previous year's leaves persistent. Leaves coriaceous, shining on both sides, glandular-serrate. Stamens 2, filaments purplish, anthers purple. Catkins appearing with the leaves.

Fens and hillsides on calcareous soils. Setesdal—Varanger, common, in some places also in the lowland. Glittertind 1750 m. Troms 1000 m.

Scandinavia, Scotland, Novaya Zemlya, N. Russia, W. Siberia.

Notes:

## 47. Northern Willow

### *Salix glauca* L.

June. Shrub 1—2 m. Leaves grey with silky hairs and plane margins. Capsules on leafy stalks, obtuse and pubescent. Differs from Downy Willow *(S. lapponum)* which has sessile catkins without leaves on the stalks and acute capsules, and from Woolly Willow *(S. lanata)* which has glabrous capsules. Catkins and leaves develop simultaneously.

Important component of the willow thickets along rivers and lakes, in damp hillsides and fens. Throughout the mountains, very common. Jotunheimen 1900 m. Troms 1200 m.

Europe (not the British Isles), Greenland, N. America, N. Asia.

46                        47

### 48. Tea-leaved Willow

*Salix phylicifolia* (L.) Sm.

May—June before the leaves. Shrub 1—2 m. Leaves thick, shining above, glaucous below, serrate except at the apex. Capsules pubescent, long-pedicellated, style long. Similar localities as the Northern Willow (no. 47). Throughout the mountains, rare in the southernmost parts. Jotunheimen 1760 m. Troms 900 m.

Europe, W. Siberia.

*Salix starkeana:* Leaves thin, glaucous below, leaf margin undulated and thin stipules. Capsules white-woolly, short pedicellated. Telemark—Trøndelag on calcareous soils. Gudbrandsdalen 1250 m.

### 49. Woolly Willow

*Salix lanata* L.

June. Shrub 1—2 m. Branches darkbrown, more or less pubescent. Leaves woolly-pubescent, large and entire, prominently veined beneath. Catkins erect, 5—10 cm, scales clothed with golden-yellow silky hairs. Similar localities as the Northern Willow *(S. glauca)* (no. 44), but not so common. Setesdal — Varanger. Jotunheimen 1750 m. Troms 1300 m.

Scandinavia, Scotland, Iceland, Arctic Russia and Siberia.

Closely related is the Gland-bearing Willow *(S. glandulifera).* Leaves narrower, glandular-serrate. Moist places. Bicentric. Sogn—S. Trøndelag. Lule Lappmark—Varanger.

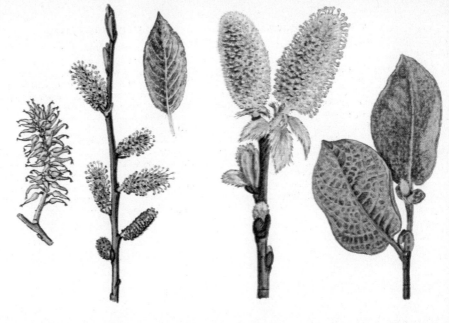

48                            49

## 50. Halbert-leaved Willow

### *Salix hastata* L.

Low shrub, often prostrate. Leaves large, thin, sharply serrated, paler below. Stipules large, serrate. Peduncles leafy. Capsules long-pedicellated, acute, glabrous, brownish-red or bright red. Moist places on calcareous soils. Telemark — Finnmark. Jotunheimen 1500 m. Troms 1120 m.

Europe, Asia, western N. America.

Small Treelike Willow *(S. arbuscula):* Leaves small, thin, glandular-serrate, stipules lacking. Capsules short-pedicellated, narrow-ovoid, white-woolly. Telemark—Finnmark, on calcareous soils, rare. Dovre 1300 m.

## 51. Dark-leaved Willow

### *Salix nigricans* Sm.

Shrub or small tree, young twigs pubescent. Leaves thin, sharply serrate, with hairs on the midvein above, turning black when dry. Capsules long-pedicellated, acute, glabrous, style long. Pedicels glabrous. Moist places throughout Scandinavia, ascending to the subalpine birch forest.

N. and M. Europe, Siberia.

Closely related is *Salix borealis* which might be regarded as an alpine race of *S. nigricans*. Leaves leathery, hairy below. Pedicels pubescent, capsules pubescent or glabrous, style short. Hardangervidda—Finnmark. Gudbrandsdalen 1250 m.

50                                        51

## 52. Dwarf Birch

*Betula nana* L.

May—June. Shrub to 1 m, usually lower and procumbent. Leaves 1 cm. Monoecious, having unisexual flowers, but both sexes on the same plant. In autumn the Dwarf Birch develops a very showy reddish colour.

Occurs in different plant communities, heaths (often dominant), fens, on the top of *Spagnum*-mounds. Does not stand a long-lasting snow cover. Throughout the mountains, very common. Also in the lowlands in moors. Jotunheimen 1570 m. Troms 1075 m.

Europe, Greenland, Labrador — Hudson Bay, N. and C. Asia.

Hybridizes with Mountain Birch (*B. tortuosa).* The hybrid is usually much taller than the Dwarf Birch. Common throughout the mountains, especially near the timber-line.

## 53. Mountain Sorrel

*Oxyria digyna* (L.) Hill

15—25 cm. July—Aug. Leaves fleshy with a fresh acidulous taste. Used by the Laps to turn reindeer milk sour. Flowers green, stamens and stigmas red. The fruit is a nut, broadly winged. Wing at first green, finally red.

Moist places, flushed snow beds, springs, ledges, often in abundance. On acid as well as on base-rich soils. Throughout the mountains, common. Jotunheimen 2150. Troms 1450 m.

Europe, Greenland, N. America, N. and C. Asia.

Notes:

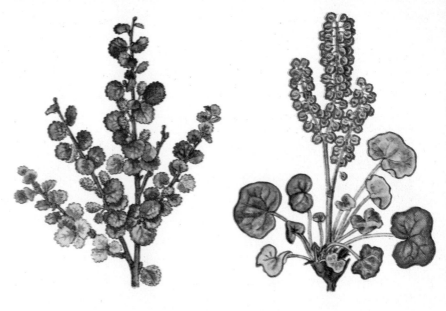

52 53

## 54. Iceland Koenigia

*Koenigia islandica* L.

3—7 cm. July—Aug. One of the few annual plants in the mountain flora of Scandinavia. Leaves smooth and fleshy. Perianth leaves usually 3, yellowish-green, stamens 3.

Wet localities on base-rich soils, fens, cold springs, snow beds, on open soil as well as in moss carpets. Hardangervidda—Varanger, not common. Dovre 1650 m. Troms 910 m.

Bipolar distribution: Arctic Europe, the Faroes, Greenland, N. America, S. America, N. and C. Asia.

Notes:

## 55. Viviparous Knotweed

*Polygonum viviparum* L.

10—25 cm. July—Aug. Flowers white or pink. The lower flowers of the spike are replaced by bulbils, rich in starch, in times of famine used for food. At high altitudes the Viviparous Knotweed does not produce seeds, reproduction only by bulbils. A small leaf often develops when the bulbil is sitting on the mother plant.

Grows in many different plant communities, dominant in early-exposed meadows on calcareous soils. Throughout Scandinavia, very common. Galdhøpiggen 2280 m. Troms 1380 m.

Europe, Greenland, N. America, N. and C. Asia.

54

55

## 56. Alpine Pearlwort

### *Sagina saginoides* (L.) Karst.

3—8 cm. Prostrate, rooting stems from a loose tuft. Flowers 5-merous, petals somewhat shorter than the sepals. Grassy hills, moist gravel and soil. Setesdal—Varanger, common. Jotunheimen 1800 m. Troms 1060 m.

Europe, Greenland, N. America, N. and C. Asia.

Lesser Alpine Pearlwort (*S. intermedia*), 2—5 cm, flowers 4-merous. Wet snow beds. Setesdal—Varanger, rare. Hardangervidda 1650 m. Troms 1380 m.

Tufted Pearlwort *(S. cæspitosa)*. Densely tufted, flowers 5-merous, petals longer than the sepals. Frost-heaving spots, wet gravel. Bicentric, very rare. Jotunheimen—Trollheimen. Salten—North Cape. Dovre 1670 m. Troms 1150 m. West-Arctic.

The *Sagina*-species have 4—5 styles.

## 57. Moss Campion

### *Silene acaulis* L.

July. Densely tufted, forming large, moss-like cushions up to a diameter of ¼ m. Cushions usually covered with short-stalked flowers. Petals rose, rarely white. The whole cushion may have a solid, very long taproot, often vertical with several cushions attached to it.

Dry as well as moist localities, particularly on mineral soil of calcareous rocks. Throughout the mountains, common. Also in the lowland on gravel bars. Jotunheimen 2210 m. Troms 1430 m.

Europe, Greenland, N. America, NE. Asia.

Notes:

56                                57

## 58. Two-flowered Sandwort

*Minuartia biflora* (L.) Sch. et Th.

5—10 cm. July—Aug. Loosely tufted, leaves narrow and obtuse. Stems glandular. Sepals blunt, 3-nerved, petals longer than sepals. Grassy meadows and gravelly spots, snow beds. Ryfylke—Varanger. Jotunheimen 2210 m. Troms 1340 m.

Europe (not the British Isles), Greenland, N. America, Asia.

## 59. Bog Sandwort

*Minuartia stricta* (Sw.) Hiern

5—15 cm. July. Leaves blunt, indistinctly nerved. Stems erect, filiform, glabrous, often violet. Sepals acute, indistinctly nerved, about the same length as the petals. Moist places, shallow fens, on calcareous soils. Hardangervidda—Varanger, rare. S. Norway 1600 m. Troms 935 m.

N. and C. Europe, Siberia, N. America, Greenland.

The *Minuartia*-species have 3 styles.

58                              59

## 60. Alpine Sandwort

*Minuartia rubella* (Wg.) Graebn.

2—8 cm. July. Densely tufted, leaves subulate, leaves subulate, strongly 3-ribbed. Upper part of the stems glandular. Sepals acute, petals white or sometimes pink, shorter than the sepals. Ledges, rocks and dry gravel on calcareous soils, rare. Bicentric. Hardanger—Røros. Nordland—Finnmark. Dovre 1450 m. Troms 1000 m.

The northern parts of Europe, America and Asia.

## 61. Norwegian Sandwort

*Arenaria norvegica* Gunn.

3—7 cm. July. Loosely tufted. Leaves glabrous, broader than in *Sagina* (no. 56) and *Minuartia* (no. 58). Dry gravel of limestone, mica schists, and olivine. Hardangervidda — W. Finnmark, very rare in S. Norway. Trollheimen 1440 m. Troms 720 m.

Scandinavia, Scotland, Shetland, Iceland.

Fringed Sandwort *(A. ciliata* ssp. *pseudofrigida)* has ciliated leaves and petals twice as long as the sepals. Calcareous gravel on the Varanger Peninsula. Besides N. Finland, Kola, Novaya Zemlya, Spitzbergen, E. Greenland.

Low Sandwort *(A. humifusa),* Pale filiform underground stolons. Flower stalks short or none at all. Northern unicentric. Hattfjelldal — North Cape, on calcareous gravel, solifluction soil, extremely rare. West-arctic.

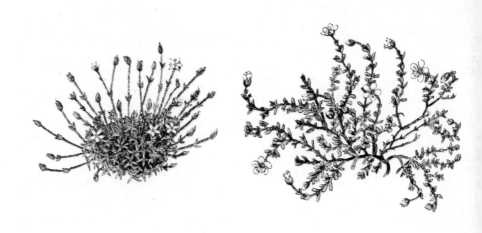

60                                  61

## 62. Starwort Mouse-ear Chickweed

### *Cerastium cerastoides* (L.) Britton

5—10 cm. Stem glabrous, creeping, shoots rooting. Flower stalks slender, glandular. Styles usually 3, in the genus *Cerastium* as a rule 5. Petals deeply bifid, twice as long as the sepals.

Preferably on snow beds permanently flushed during the summer, cold springs, more rarely in fens. Throughout the mountains, very common. Jotunheimen 2040 m. Troms 1185 m.

Europe, Greenland, NE. America, C. Asia, Atlas.

Notes:

## 63. Alpine Mouse-ear Chickweed

### *Cerastium alpinum* L.

10—20 cm. July—Aug. Petals not very deeply bifid. Bracts with membranous margins. Stems and leaves pubescent. A glabrous form, var. *glabratum,* may be regarded as a separate species. Meadows, heaths and ledges. Var. *glabratum* on calcareous soils and olivine. Setesdal—Varanger, common. Galdhøpiggen 2220 m. Troms 1450 m. Europe, Greenland. arctic N. America.

Arctic Mouse-ear Chickweed *(C. arcticum).* Bracts green, sepals blunt, leaves more broadly elliptical and denser than in *C. alpinum.* Forming tufts on wet, gravelly snow beds on calcareous soils. Bicentric. Hardangervidda—Trollheimen. Nordland—Finnmark. Jotunheimen 2245 m. Troms 1400 m. West-arctic. Closely related to *C. edmonstonii* known from Snowdon, Scotland and Inner Hebrides.

62                                    63

## 64. Wood Chickweed

*Stellaria nemorum* L.

20—40 cm. July. Stoloniferous with subterranean stolons as well. Stems and leaves somewhat pubescent. Lower leaves long stalked cordate. Petals deeply bifid. Luxuriant and moist places in birch forest, willow thickets and along creeks. Throughout the mountains, common. Also in the lowland. S. Norway 1400 m. Troms 750 m.

Europe, Caucasus, SW. Siberia.

## 65. Northern Starwort

*Stellaria calycantha* (Led.) Bong.

15—30 cm. Petals usually wanting, or 2—3, shorter than the sepals. Flower stalks long, finally drooping. Stems lax. Moist localities in birch forests and willow thickets. Setesdal—Varanger, rare in the western districts. S. Norway 1400 m. Troms 710 m.

Scandinavia, N. Russia, Iceland, Greenland, N. America, in Asia only in the easternmost and westernmost parts of N. Siberia.

Notes:

64                                    65

## 66. Red Campion

### *Melandrium rubrum* (Weig.) Garcke

20—30 cm. June—July. Stem long-pubescent. Lower leaves stalked, upper one sessile. Dioecious. Female individuals with inflated calyx, male plants with narrow calyx. Petals sometimes pink, more rarely white. Throughout Scandinavia, but rare in the northeasternmost parts. Variabel. The mountain plants are short-grown with large flowers. Occurs in numerous plant communities, subalpine birch forests, willow thickets and meadows in the low-alpine regions. Similar to no. 68 abundantly on slag. Jotunheimen 1780 m. Troms 1038 m.

Europe, N. Asia, N. Africa.

## 67. Nodding Lychnis

### *Melandrium apetalum* (L.) Fenzl.

10—20 cm. July—Aug. Flower at first nodding, later erect. Calyx strongly inflated. Petals usually small and reduced, purplish, included within or very rarely exceeding the calyx, which is contracted at the top. Moist places, particularly on north-facing slopes, grassy meadows, *Dryas*-heaths, only on calcareous soils. Bicentric. Hardangervidda — Sylene. Hattfjelldal—W. Finnmark. Jotunheimen 1970 m. Troms 1055 m.

N. Europe, Greenland, N. America, N. and C. Asia.

Arctic Lychnis *(M. angustiflorum)* is smaller than *M. apetalum*. Calyx less inflated, petals white and exserted. Upper part of stem glandular. Northern unicentric, very rare.

66                    67

## 68. Red Alpine Catchfly

*Viscaria alpina* (L.) G. Don

10—15 cm. Stems solitary or several together, not viscid. Flowers *Linnaea*-scented. Petals deeply bifid with coronal scales at the base of the limb.

Exposed heaths together with *Juncus trifidus* and *Festuca ovina,* ledges, open gravel. In particular it occurs abundantly on slag near pyrites mines, often predominating on olivine and serpentine rocks, prefers soils rich in pyrites and heavy metals. Throughout the mountains, common, in some places also in the lowland. Jotunheimen 1900 m. Troms 1030 m.

Europe, Greenland, NE. Canada, N. Asia.

Notes:

## 69. Alpine Meadow Rue

*Thalictrum alpinum* L.

10—15 cm. Stem slender and wiry, glabrous. Leaves dark green above, whitish below. Filaments usually violet, anthers brownish yellow, in northern areas the filaments may be pale yellow and the anthers yellow. *Dryas*-heaths, fens, ledges, on calcareous soils. Setesdal—Finnmark, common. Jotunheimen 2000 m. Troms 1100 m.

Europe, Greenland, N. America, N. and C. Asia.

68

69

## 70. Globe Flower

### *Trollius europæus* L.

30—50 cm. July. Leaves palmately 3—5 lobed, with lobes deeply cut. Flowers 3 cm diam., slightly fragrant, usually solitary or 2—3 together. Ligulate nectaries hidden between the stamens and the sepals. Stamens and carpels numerous.

Wet pastures, grassland and hillsides. Particularly abundant on base-rich soils in subalpine areas in N. Scandinavia. Sogn—Varanger, lacking in the western districts. In E. Norway and Sweden also in the lowland. Dovre 1080 m. Troms 1220 m.

Europe, Caucasus, W. Siberia.

Notes:

## 71. Monkshood

### *Aconitum septentrionale* Koelle

75 cm—1,5 m. July. Vigorous branched tuberous stock. Stem coarse, hollow, downy. Leaves large, palmately 3—5-partite. Raceme 20—40 cm, the flowers (the sepals) sometimes become white or yellowish. Curved nectaries on long stalks (two of the petals) in the helmet. The whole plant is highly poisonous, especially the root. Has been used against insects, i.a. lice (cf. the Norwegian name «lousehat»). Visited by long-tongued bumblebees.

Sub-alpine birch forest and willow thickets on rich soils, rare above the timber line. Telemark—Troms, lacking in the western mountains of S. Norway. S. Norway 1670 m.

Europe, Asia.

70             71

## 72. Glacier Buttercup

*Ranunculus glacialis* L.

10—15 cm. July—Aug. The colour of the petals changes from white to pink and finally to deeply purplish. Sepals with reddish-brown hairs. Leaves fleshy. The flowers are eaten by reindeer. One of the commonest species at high altitudes, rarely descending to the timber line.

Snow beds, mineral soil, solifluction and frost heaving soils, mountain tops, also in heaths where it develops early in summer while the ground is still moist. Hardangervidda—Finnmark. Altitude record-holder among phanerogams in Scandinavia as well in the Alps. Galdhøpiggen 2370 m. Troms 1636 m. Finsteraarhorn (the Alps) 4275 m.

Europe, the Faroes, Iceland, Jan Mayen, Spitzbergen, Greenland.

Notes:

## 73. White Buttercup

*Ranunculus platanifolius* L.

0,5—1 m. July—Aug. Basal leaves palmately divided, long-stalked. Inflorescence few-flowered, flowers long-stalked. Petals and sepals readily falling.

A characteristic species of luxuriant subalpine hillsides together with Blue Snow-Thistle, Monkshood and Melancholy Thistle. Willow thickets and south-facing slopes above the timber line. Setesdal—Rana and Åsele Lappmark. In addition a peculiar isolated locality on the island of Sørøya in Finnmark. S. Norway 1400 m.

Known only from Scandinavia and the mountains of C. and S. Europe.

72                                           73

### 74. Arctic Buttercup

*Ranunculus hyperboreus* Rottb.

5 cm. July—Aug. Poisonous and used as arrow poison by the Indians and the Eskimos in Canada. Wet places, springs, often floating in small ponds. Mountain farms in manured places. Bicentric. Hallingdal—Jämtland. Arctic Circle—Varanger. Dovre 1560 m. Troms 760 m.

The northern districts of Europe, America and Asia, Greenland.

### 75. Pigmy Buttercup

*Ranunculus pygmœus* Wg.

3—5 cm. July—Aug. Prostrate — ascending. Wet snow beds, often abundant. Throughout the mountains, Jotunheimen 2230 m. Troms 1450 m.

N. Europe, very rare in the Alps. Greenland, N. America, N. Siberia.

Notes:

### 76. Snow Buttercup

*Ranunculus nivalis* L.

5—10 cm. June—July. Petals yellowish-green while young, later on pure yellow, sepals with reddish-brown hairs. Flushed snow beds, preferably on calcareous soils. Slightly bicentric. Valdres—Jämtland, rare. Namdalen—Varanger, common. Dovre 1550 m. Troms 1450 m.

N. Europe, Greenland, arctic N. America, N. Siberia.

Sulphur-coloured Buttercup *(R. sulphureus)* is somewhat taller, flowers sulphur-coloured. Basal leaf-blades fleshy, at the base cuneiform. Similar localities as the Snow Buttercup. Northern unicentric. Torne Lappmark—Varanger, rare. Troms 1050 m. Arctic parts of Europe and America, N. and C. Asia.

74 75 76

## 77. Spring Pasque Flower

*Anemone vernalis* L.

10—15 cm. May—June. Leaves persistent, hairy. The stem, leafy bracts and outside of the perianth with silky hairs. After flowering the stem elongates. Achenes with persistent hairy styles when in fruit, forming a characteristic head or brush. Wind dispersal with the hairy style as the organ of flight. Poisonous.

Dry plains and heaths. Hallingdal—Trollheimen, rare, common also in some places in the lowlands in E. Norway and S. and C. Sweden. Jotunheimen 1860 m. Europe, W. Siberia.

## 78. Arctic Poppy

*Papaver radicatum* Rottb.

10—20 cm. July. The plants contain a milky juice easily seen when the petiole is cut. The species is split up in several subspecies, many of them endemic in Scandinavia, and with a very restricted distribution. Scree slopes, gravel bars and ledges, only on base-rich soils. The species taken in a broad sense bicentric. Valdres—Trollheimen. Saltdal—Varanger, Dovre 1850 m. Troms 1340 m.

Arctic Europe, the Faroes, Iceland, Greenland, arctic N. America.

In North Scandinavia several closely related species. *Papaver læstadianum,* endemic in a small area at the point where Finland, Sweden and Norway meet. *P. lapponicum:* Kvænangen and Talvik. *P. dahlianum:* Varanger Peninsula. Flowers both yellow and white. This is the poppy of Spitzbergen.

77

78

## 79. White Arctic Whitlow-grass

*Draba fladnizensis* Wulf.

2—10 cm. June—July. Leaves ciliate with simple hairs, stems and fruits glabrous. Dry ridges and tops. Bicentric, rare. Hallingdal—Budal. Saltdal — W. Finnmark. Galdhøpiggen 2300 m. Troms 1160 m. Europe, Greenland, N. America, N. and C. Asia.

The same size have:

1. Lapland Whitlow-grass *(D. lactea)*. Leaves with stellate hairs on the surface, simple hairs at the margins, stem glabrous. Bicentric, very rare.
2. Snow Witlow-grass *(D. nivalis)*. Leaves and stems grey with minute stellate hairs. Fruits narrow. Bicentric, very rare.
3. Norwegian Whitlow-grass *(D. norvegica)*. Leaves and stems with simple, bifurcate and stellate hairs.

Dovre Whitlow-grass *(D. dovrensis)* and Smoothing Whitlow-grass *(D. daurica)* are taller, 20—40 cm, the former with hairy fruits, southern unicentric, the latter with glabrous fruits, bicentric. All *Draba*'s mentioned here are white-flowered and grow on calcareous soils.

## 80. Alpine Whitlow-grass

*Draba alpina* L.

5—15 cm. June—July. Leaves pubescent with simple and forked hairs. Stems and pedicels shaggy-hirsute, fruits spreading, glabrous or sparsely hairy. Moist places, particularly on north-facing slopes, snow beds, ledges, on calcareous soils. Bicentric, rare. Valdres—Meråker. Hattfjelldal—Nordreisa. Dovre 1700 m. Troms 1200 m. Arctic Europe, Greenland, arctic N. America, N. and C. Asia.

Thick-leaved Whitlow-grass *(D. crassifolia)*, 2—5 cm. Petals sulphur-yellow, the plant almost glabrous. Snow beds and moist gravel on calcareous soils. Northern unicentric, very rare. Hattfjelldal—Nordreisa. Only in this area in Europe. West-arctic.

79                                          80

## 81. Alpine Cress

### *Cardamine bellidifolia* L.

3—7 cm. Tufted. Leaves shiny. Stems short, elongating when the fruit is ripening. Flowers white on short stalks not overtopping the leaves. Fruits erect, ca. 3 cm. Wet gravel, solifluction soil, snow beds, top plateaus, often associated with the Glacier Buttercup. Throughout the mountains, common. Jotunheimen 2200 m. Troms 1480 m.

N. Europe, N. America, N. and C. Asia. Polar Cress *(C. nymanii):* Leaves thick, basal ones with 3—7 rounded leaflets. Petals rose. Often sterile. Wet snow beds on calcareous soils. Dovre 1600 m. Troms 780 m.

## 82. Alpine Rock-cress

### *Arabis alpina* L.

10—20 cm. June—July. Loosely tufted, stems and leaves usually with simple and stellate hairs, rarely a glabrous form occurs, var. *glabrata*. Flowers slightly violet-scented. Fruits 3 cm, spreading-erect.

Moist, gravelly and flushed snow beds, creek beds, ledges, particularly on northfacing slopes. Often abundant. Throughout the mountains, common. Jotunheimen 1980 m. Troms 1400 m.

Europe, Greenland, arctic NE. Canada, arctic Siberia east to Jenisej River. Popular rock-garden plant.

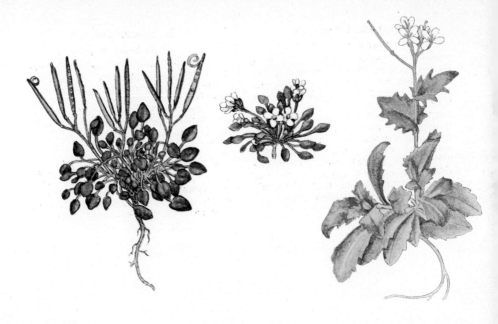

81                                    82

## 83. Northern Rock-cress

*Cardaminopsis petræa* (L.) Hiit.

10—20 cm. July. The leaves of the basal rosettes variable, usually pinnatifid, but may also be entire. Usually hairy, but also glabrous. Flowers white or with a purplish tinge.

Scree slopes, gravel bars and rock crevices, in W. Norway descending to sea level. The species has a peculiar distribution in Scandinavia. In Norway it is distributed from Ryfylke to Trollheimen, rare. Jotunheimen 1700 m. In Sweden it has an isolated area in Ångermanland at the Gulf of Bothnia where it grows on gravelly shores.

Europe.

Notes:

## 84. Smoothing Braya

*Braya linearis* Rouy

5—15 cm. Tufted with a stout yellowish-brown tap-root. Stems softly hairy with few leaves. Petals rose-coloured, sepals purplish red. Fruits long, somewhat constricted between the seeds. Scree slopes and ledges, only on calcareous soils. Bicentric. In S. Norway only in Jotunheimen. In the north from Bindal to W. Finnmark, rare. Troms 800 m. Nearest localities on E. Greenland.

Purplish Braya *(B. purpurascens)* has its single locality in Scandinavia in the island of Magerøya near North Cape. Petals pale purple, stem without leaves. Known from the arctic parts of Europe, America and Asia.

83                                   84

## 85. Rose-root

### *Sedum rosea* (L.) Scop.

10—25 cm. July. Stock branched, thick, fleshy, inside yellow, rose-scented. Stems in a dense cluster. Leaves succulent. The sexes on different plants. Each female flower has 4 carpels which redden gradually. The stock has been used for food and for medicinal purposes, and a decoction as a shampoo (cf. the Norwegian name: 'growth of the hair'). It has often been planted on turf-covered roofs in the belief that it affords protection against lightning and fire.

Willow thickets, meadows and heaths, fens and ledges. Throughout the mountains, common. In W. Norway down to sea level. Galdhøpiggen 2280 m. Troms 1380 m.

Europe, Greenland, N. America, A. and C. Asia.

Notes:

## 86. Hairy Stonecrop

### *Sedum villosum* L.

5—10 cm. July—Aug. Stems and leaves viscid and glandular-hairy. Leaves linear, obtuse, succulent. Flowers at first pink, often becoming purplish like the whole plant. Reproduction by stalked bulbils arising in the axils of the leaves and readily detached.

Found particularly in swelling moss carpets at cold springs, fens and wet ledges. Slightly bicentric, rare. Hardanger—Jotunheimen. Sylene—North Cape. Jotunheimen 1880 m.

Europe, Greenland, N. Africa.

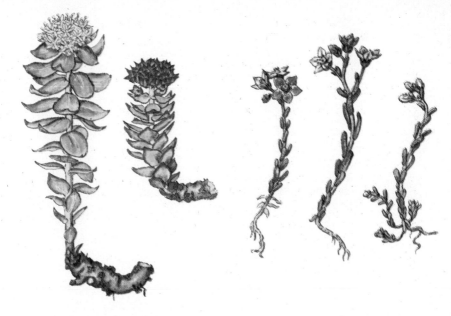

85                                          86

## 87. Mountain Queen

*Saxifraga cotyledon* L.

20—40 cm. July. Basal rosettes of leaves up to 10 cm. Stolons radiating from the central rosette form new terminal rosettes. Leaves succulent, toothed, the teeth covered by a crust of lime deposited by the evaporation of calcareous water from the leaves. *S. cotyledon* becomes very tall and magnificent when growing on steep cliffs and ledges. It occurs also on dry ridges in the mountains.

Throughout the mountains to W. Finnmark. Rare or lacking in the eastern mountains. In N. Norway down to sea level. Trollheimen 1320 m.

Only in Scandinavia, the Alps, the Carpathians, the Pyrenees and Iceland.

Livelong Saxifrage *(S. paniculata)* is smaller, few-flowered, branches short and stiff. The European subspecies in S. Norway (Ryfylke), an endemic subspecies in N. Norway (Saltdal).

## 88. Purple Saxifrage

*Saxifraga oppositifolia* L.

May—Aug. Loosely matted or tufted with somewhat woody branches. In steep localities long draping shoots are formed. The tip of the leaves covered with a crust of lime. Flowers immediately after exposure early in spring, continuing during the whole summer in later exposed localities.

In different kinds of plant communities on calcareous soils, predominating on late snow beds. Throughout the mountains, common. In W. and N. Norway down to sea level. Galdhøpiggen 2350 m. Troms 1675 m.

Europe, Greenland, N. America, N. and C. Asia. On the north coast of Greenland, 83°15', the most northerly-plant locality in the world.

87                                                 88

## 89. Alpine Saxifrage

*Saxifraga nivalis* L.

10—15 cm. July—Aug. Stems stout, pubescent. Leaves thick. Flowers in dense head-like inflorescence. Carpels 2, beaked. On crevices and ledges, preferably on base-rich soils. Throughout the mountains, common. Jotunheimen 2250 m. Troms 1510 m.

Europe, Greenland, arctic N. America, Siberia.

Slender Saxifraga *(S. tenuis)* is more slender, 3—8 cm, stems glandular, inflorescence more open, the beak of the fruit curved backwards. Wet snow beds, preferably on calcareous soils. Throughout the mountains. Jotunheimen 2000 m. Troms 1450 m. West-arctic.

Hawkweed-leaved Saxifrage *(S. hieracifolia),* 10—25 cm. stems rigid, leaves ovate, flower purple. Bicentric, very rare. Jotunheimen—Sunndalen. Troms—W. Finnmark, Europe, Greenland, N. America.

## 90. Ascending Saxifrage

*Saxifraga adscendens* L.

15—25 cm. Biennial. June—July. Leaves glandular-pubescent. Flowers usually white, rarely pink or sulphureous yellow. Crevices, dry rocks, screes, *Dryas*-heaths, preferably on calcareous soils. Ryfylke—Troms. S. Norway 1600 m. Troms 600 m.

Europe, Caucasus, N. America.

## 91. Drooping Saxifrage

*Saxifraga cernua* L.

10—20 cm. July—Aug. Usually a single terminal flower. Reproduction by means of brownish-red bulbils in the axils of the leaves. Moist places, snow beds, ledges, preferably on calcareous soils. Ryfylke—Varanger, common. Galdhøpiggen 2350 m. Troms 1450 m.

Europe, Greenland, N. America, N. and C. Asia.

89            90            91

## 92. Starry Saxifrage

*Saxifraga stellaris* L.

5—12 cm. July—Aug. Petals white with two yellow or red spots near the base or sometimes unspotted. Anthers red or yellow. Wet places, snow beds, fens, in springs and by brooks. Throughout the mountains, very common. Glittertind 1970 m. Troms 1390 m.

Europe, Greenland, Labrador.

Foliolose Saxifrage *(S. foliolosa)* is closely related. Usually only one terminal flower (or none at all), the other flowers replaced by clusters of small brownish-green leaves (bulbils) functioning as reproductive units. Moist soil and gravel, preferably on calcareous soils. Jotunheimen—Varanger, but rare in S. Norway. Troms 1580 m. Europe, Greenland, N. America, N. Asia.

## 93. Yellow Mountains-Saxifrage

*Saxifraga aizoides* L.

5—15 cm. July—Aug. Plant matted or tufted. The colour of the˙ flowers variable. Usually the petals are yellow with orange spots and the anthers orange, but quite often the petals are orange with red spots and the anthers red. More rarely specimens are found with scarlet petals while the other parts of the flower are more or less reddish-brown.

Moist places, by springs and brooks, gravel bars, irrigated slopes and cliffs, often very abundant, preferably on base-rich soils. Throughout the mountains, common. Jotunheimen 1700 m. Troms 1440 m.

Europe, Greenland, eastern N. America, Rocky Mts, W. Asia.

92                                                      93

## 94. Brook Saxifrage

*Saxifraga rivularis* L.

2—6 cm. July—Aug. Often in small tufts. Stem with underground bulbils and often with rooting stolons producing new rosettes. Reproduction also by seeds. Usually the petals are white and the anthers yellow, but rarely a form occurs with all parts of the flower reddish.

Flushed snow beds, by brooks and cold springs, especially where luxuriant moss carpets are developed. Setesdal—Varanger, common. Jotunheimen 2350 m. Troms 1480 m.

Scandinavia, arctic Russia, Scotland, Iceland, Greenland, N. America, N. Asia.

Notes:

## 95. Tufted Saxifrage

*Saxifraga cespitosa* L.

5—12 cm. July—Aug. Dense cushions from a stout tap-root. Withered, dead leaves below the living ones. Leaves, stems and sepals clothed with glandular hairs. The colour of the petals varies from pure white to yellowish.

Dry places, preferably on base-rich soils, *Dryas*-heaths, exposed ridges, by cairns and on tops manured by birds. Setesdal—Varanger, common. In W. and N. Norway down to sea level. Galdhøpiggen 2280 m. Troms 1450 m.

Europe, Greenland, N. America, N. Asia.

94                                   95

## 96. Grass of Parnassus

*Parnassia palustris* L.

8—15 cm. July—Aug. Stems as well as leaves glabrous. Of the ten stamens five are replaced by staminodes with nectaries on the upper surface. Each staminode is split into many hair-like lobes each ending in a shining yellowish-green gland.

Meadows and fens, ledges, also in dry *Dryas*-heaths and on exposed ridges. In the mountains it prefers base-rich soils. Common throughout Scandinavia, also in the lowlands. Jotunheimen 1700 m. Troms 1070 m. The species is very variable.

Europe, N. Africa, N. America, A. and C. Asia.

Notes:

## 97. Cloudberry

*Rubus chamœmorus* L.

10—20 cm. June. Creeping rhizome. Flowers monoecious. The flowering is very variable from one year to another, in some years the female plant rests. Drupelets pleasant-tasting. Seed-dispersal by birds and bears, etc. Throughout Scandinavia, common. S. Norway 1400 m. Troms 1115 m.

Europe, Greenland, N. America, N. and C. Asia.

Arctic Bramble *(Rubus arcticus)* lacks the vegetative shoots, leaves trifoliate, flowers red (rarely white), drupelets red, pleasant-tasting. Flowers later than the cloudberry. July—Aug. Willow thickets and grassy places, especially in the birch region. Eastern species, rare, except in Finnmark. Hallingdal—Valdres. Jotunheimen 1150 m. N. Norway 500 m. Northern parts of Europe, Asia and America (not Greenland and Iceland).

96

97

## 98. Snow Cinquefoil

### *Potentilla nivea* L.

10—15 cm. July. Stock firm with brown remnants of leaves. Leaves densely white-tomentose beneath. Stems and petioles tomentose. Particularly found on the driest and most exposed ridges and rocks, in scree slopes and crevices, only on base-rich soils. Bicentric, rare. Hardangervidda—Sylene. Nordland—Varanger. Jotunheimen 1700 m. Troms 1060 m.

Scandinavia, the Alps, Greenland, N. America, N. and C. Asia.

Lapland Cinquefoil *(P. chamissonis)* is closely related. Petioles with straight hairs. Crevices and ledges. Northern unicentric, very rare. Lule Lappmark—Finnmark. West-arctic.

Notes:

## 99. Alpine Cinquefoil

### *Potentilla crantzii* (Cr.) Beck.

7—15 cm. July. Stems softly hairy. The mountain race differs from the lowland one in its larger flowers (2 cm). Quite often the basal leaves are ternate, otherwise they are palmate with 5 leaflets. Grows in most of the different plant communities exposed not too late, grassland (meadows and heaths), *Dryas*-heaths, ledges, scree slopes. Throughout the mountains, common. Jotunheimen 2210 m. Troms 1270 m.

Europe, Greenland, N. America, N. and C. Asia.

Arctic Cinquefoil *(P. hyparctica)* is found in Lule Lappmark near the Norwegian border. Leaves ternate with long hairs in the margins. Petals lacking orange spots. Heath and solifluction soil, calciphilous. 1440 m. Arctic. Nearest localities on Spitzbergen.

98                              99

## 100. Mountains Avens

### *Dryas octopetala* L.

July. Evergreen prostrate undershrub forming large mats. Stems tortuose, diameter up to 1 cm, may grow very old. Leaves green and glabrous above, denselv white-tomentose beneath. Flower stalks 3—10 cm. Style persistent on the fruit with white feathery hairs, functioning as a dispersal agent.

A very good indicator of base-rich soils. On dry, early exposed heaths of loose schists and limestone it often predominates, forming the *Dryas*-heaths, a plant community very rich in species. Setesdal—Varanger, in N. Norway and a few places in S. Norway also in the lowland. Jotunheimen 2275 m. Troms 1260 m.

Europe, Greenland, Alaska, N. Asia.

Notes:

## 101. Procumbent Sibbaldia

### *Sibbaldia procumbens* L.

3—10 cm. July—Aug. Stock woody, clothed with withered remains of dead leaves. Flower-stems ofte prostrate. First leaves entire, later ternate, softly hairy beneath. The plant needs several years in order to develop flowers.

Willow thickets, meadows and especially in grassy snow beds, often very abundant. Throughout the mountains, common. In N. and W. Norway descending to sea level. Jotunheimen 2130 m. Troms 1300 m.

Europe, Greenland, N. America, N. and C. Asia.

100 101

## 102. Alpine Lady's Mantle

*Alchemilla alpina* L.

July—Aug. Stock branched, woody, with brown remnants of previous years' leaves, the branches ending in leaf rosettes. Leaves glabrous above, silvery-silky beneath. Flower stalks 10—20 cm. Flowers in dense clusters, petals lacking, sepals 4, yellowish green. Reproduction by seed without a sexual fusion (apomixis).

Often dominant on early exposed snow beds, preferably on acid soils. Throughout the mountains, common. Descending to sea level in W. and N. Norway. Jotunheimen 1760 m. Troms 975 m.

Europe, Caucasus, Iceland, Greenland.

Notes:

## 103. Cluster-flowered Lady's Mantle

*Alchemilla glomerulans* Bus.

15—25 cm. July. Belongs to a difficult and critical group. Apomictic (seed not developed from a sexual fusion). Stems and petioles with silky appressed hairs. Leaves hairy above. Teeth broad, 13—15 on each lobe. Often dominant on moist snow beds. By creeks and springs, willow thickets. Throughout the mountains, common. Dovre 1500 m. Troms 1020 m.

Europe, Iceland, Greenland, Labrador.

Glabrous Lady's Mantle *(A. glabra):* Leaves glabrous. The terminal tooth on each lobe smaller than the other ones.

Wichura's Lady's Mantle *(A. wichurae):* Leaves orbicular. The sinus between the lobes narrowly V-shaped.

Murbeck's Lady's Mantle *(A. murbeckiana):* Leaves reniform (kidney-shaped) with acute lobes.

102

103

## 104. Alpine Milk-vetch

*Astragalus alpinus* L.

10—20 cm. July—Aug. Variable species. Flowers pale blue or purplish blue (rarely white). In N. Scandinavia, another form occurs with purple flowers (subsp. *arcticus).* Fragrant. The pod does not open, the seeds are dispersed when the pod blows away and is torn to pieces. Resembling Lapland Oxytropis (*Oxytropis lapponica),* but the leaflets are blunt, whereas in the Lapland Oxytropis they are acute.

Meadows, gravel bars, *Dryas*-heaths, often abundant. Descending along the streams to the lowland. Throughout the mountains, common. Jotunheimen 1700 m. Troms 1380 m.

Europe, N. America, A. and C. Asia.

## 105. Arctic Milk-vetch

*Astragalus frigidus* (L.) A. Gray

Formerly named *Phaca frigida* L. 10—30 cm. July—Aug. Flower-stalks, calyx-teeth and pods with black hairs. As in no. 104 the seeds loosen in the pods which are shed unopened. The name Milk-vetch indicates that these leguminous species are considered valuable fodder plants.

Meadows, solifluction soil, fens, willow thickets, birch forests, preferably on calcareous soils. Slightly bicentric, not common. Jotunheimen—Meråker. Lycksele Lappmark —Varanger. Trollheimen 1300 m. Troms 1000 m.

Europe, N. and C. Asia.

104

105

## 106. Norwegian Milk-vetch

*Astragalus norvegicus* Grauer

15—30 cm. July—Aug. More stiff and erect than no. 104. The colour of the flowers variable, usually blue, sometimes whitish-lilac to reddish-purple. No scent. In contrast with nos. 104 and 105 the pods open, but the seeds remain fastened to the valves. When the dry pods blow away, the seeds are shaken free little by little.

*Dryas*-heaths, willow thickets, fens and birch forests, only on base-rich soils. Jotunheimen—Varanger, in the northernmost parts very rare. Trollheimen 1420 m. Lule Lappmark 1070 m.

Europe, Siberia.

Notes:

## 107. Lapland Oxytropis

*Oxytropis lapponica* (Wg.) Gay

5—15 cm. July—Aug. Stems often prostrate. The petals purple, later pale bluish-purple, finally dirty grey. The pods open in the upper part forming a horizontal shovel. The seeds are attached by small hairs. If the shovel gets a push from above, the seeds loosen and when the elastic flower stalk flies back, they are thrown out.

Dry ridges and heaths, scree slopes, on base-rich soils. Hardangervidda—Porsanger, quite rare. Finse 1555 m. Troms 1100 m.

Europe, N. and C. Asia.

Pendent Oxytropis *(O. deflexa)* has impure white flowers in a long raceme. Kautokeino, the only locality in Europe.

106         107

## 108. Kidney-vetch

*Anthyllis vulneraria* L.

10—15 cm. July. Stems decumbent, pubescent. Flowers densely capitate. Calyx woolly-pubescent, inflated, persistent. Pod enclosed in and shed together with the calyx, the whole unit dispersed by the wind.

Dry ridges, heaths, ledges, screes and open gravel, preferably on calcareous soils. The mountain race (var. *lapponica)* differs slightly from the lowland ones.

Setesdal—W. Finnmark, not common. Hardangervidda 1350 m. Troms 500 m.

Europe, N. Africa, Caucasus, Iceland.

Notes:

## 109. Wood Cranesbill

*Geranium sylvaticum* L.

30—40 cm. June—July. Basal leaves usually deeply 7-parted, the upper ones almost sessile. Flowers in two. The colour of the flowers very variable from dark violet to pink or almost white. The stamens are ripe before the styles. In this way self-pollination is avoided.

Throughout Scandinavia and very common in the mountains in sub-alpine birch forests, willow thickets and low-alpine meadows. Jotunheimen 1750 m. Troms 1000 m.

Europe, Asia Minor, Siberia.

108                                109

### 110. Two-flowered Violet

*Viola biflora* L.

5—15 cm. July. The brown veins on the lower petal may show the insects the entrance to the nectaries in the spur.

Moist places in the low-alpine region, snow beds, willow thickets, birch forests. Throughout the mountains, very common. In the north and in some places in the south descending to the lowland. Dovre 1500 m. Troms 1270 m.

Europe, N. America, Asia.

Marsh Violet (*V. palustris*), 5—10 cm, is a lowland species frequently found in the mountains as well. Flowers lilac with darker veins, leaves reniform, denticulate. Throughout Scandinavia, common. Jotunheimen 1750 m. Troms 925 m. Europe, Greenland, N. America.

### 111. Hornemann's Willow-herb

*Epilobium hornemannii* Rchb.

10—15 cm. July—Aug. Short, underground, rosette-like stolons with fleshy scales. Leaves thin, dark green, sparsely denticulate, obtuse. Seeds tubercled. By springs and brooks. Throughout the mountains, common. Jotunheimen 1800 m. Sarek 1060 m.

Northern Europe, NE. Asia, N. America, Greenland.

110                                   111

### 112. Dahurian Willow-herb

*Epilobium davuricum* Fisch.

10—20 cm. July—Aug. Stems slightly pubescent. No stolons. Flowers white or pink. Fens and springs on base-rich soils. Hardanger—Varanger, rare. Hardangervidda 1360 m. Troms 520 m.

N. Europe, arctic N. America, N. Asia.

Marsh Willow-herb *(E. palustre)* has long filiform stolons terminating in a bulbil-like bud. Stems with 2 rows of hairs. Flowers pale rose or lilac. Fens. Throughout Scandinavia, common. Hardangervidda 1320 m.

### 113. Alpine Willow-herb

*Epilobium anagallidifolium* Lam.

3—10 cm. July—Aug. Prostrate aboveground stolons with distant small green leaves. Stem strongly curved, when ripe the stalk and the capsule are erect. Usually a single flower. Seeds smooth. Wet snow beds. Throughout the mountains, common. Jotunheimen 1800 m. Troms 1040 m.

Europe, Greenland, N. America, N. and C. Asia.

### 114. Chickweed Willow-herb

*Epilobium alsinifolium* Vill.

15—25 cm. July—Aug. Stems with 2 rows of hairs. Long underground stolons with fleshy, pale scales terminating in a round bud. Seeds minutely tuberculate. By brooks and cold springs. Setesdal—Varanger, common. Hardangervidda 1350 m. Troms 890 m.

Europe, Iceland, Greenland.

Milky-flowered Willow-herb *(E. lactiflorum)* has smaller leaves, white flowers and short rosette-like stolons. Moist slopes, meadows. Setesdal—Varanger. Jotunheimen 1660 m. West-arctic.

112          113          114

## 115. Dwarf Cornel

*Cornus suecica* L.

10—20 cm. June—July. Underground creeping rhizome. Leaves deciduous. «The flower» is in reality an umbel-like inflorescence surrounded by 4 large, white bracts, at times somewhat greenish beneath. Each true flower consists of 4 small brownish-black petals and 4 stamens. Fruit a drupe, spongy and tasteless, but not poisonous.

In the lowland as well as in the birch region of the mountains, often very abundant. Throughout Scandinavia. S. Norway 1200 m. Troms and Finnmark 600 m.

NW. Europe, Greenland, NE. Canada, both sides of the Bering Strait.

## 116. Garden Angelica

*Angelica archangelica* L.

0,5—1 m. July—Aug. Plant stout, rootstock thick, stem hollow. Petioles shallowly or indistinctly grooved. Umbels 10—20 cm in diameter. The whole plant with a strong smell when rubbed. Flowers fragrant, attracting numerous and different small insects. Formerly an important vegetable and also used for medicinal purposes. Sub-alpine birch forests, willow thickets, by springs and brooks, on rich soil. Throughout the mountains. Jotunheimen 1600 m. Troms 1070 m.

Europe, Siberia, Greenland.

Wild Angelica *(A. sylvestris)* also occurs in the birch forests. It is less stout, the stem is finely pubescent and the petioles are distinctly grooved.

115  116

## 117. Common Wintergreen

### *Pyrola minor* L.

7—15 cm. Leaves coriaceous, evergreen, crenulate and glandular along the whole margin. Style straight, included in the flower. Calyx lobes triangular.

Birch forests, willow thickets, bilberry-heaths, meadows. Throughout Scandinavia, common. Jotunheimen 1620 m. Troms 900 m.

Europe, Greenland, N. America, N. and C. Asia.

Intermediate Wintergreen *(P. media)* sometimes ascends to the birch region. Stouter than Common Wintergreen, leaves almost entire-margined, style straight, exserted, calyx lobes ovate. Throughout Scandinavia. S. Norway 1000 m. Europe, Asia Minor.

Notes:

## 118. Norwegian Wintergreen

### *Pyrola norvegica* G. Knaben

10—20 cm. July—Aug. Leaves crenulate. Style long and strongly curved, green. Lower part of calyx with a greenish-white collar. Closely related to the lowland species Larger Wintergreen *(P. rotundifolia)* which lacks the collar, and has a red style.

Birch forests, willow thickets, fens. *Dryas*-heaths, on calcareous soils. Throughout the mountains, quite common. Jotunheimen 1500 m. Troms 915 m. The species known only from Scandinavia. It is most closely related to Arctic Wintergreen *(P. grandiflora)* (perhaps the same species), which occurs in Greenland and in the arctic parts of N. America and Asia.

117                                        118

## 119. Louiseleuria

*Loiseleuria procumbens* (L.) Desv.

Procumbent under-shrub forming extensive tufts and mats. Leaves evergreen, coriaceous, well protected against desiccation. Flowers in bud rose-coloured, later pink, rarely white.

Loiseleuria is a very characteristic plant of exposed ridges and heaths, particularly on acid soils. The localities are very dry in summer, and in winter the snow cover is scarce or lacking (cf. no. 125). One of the spring-flowering plants of the mountains, June. Throughout the mountains, very common. Jotunheimen 1920 m, Troms 1150 m.

Europe, Greenland, N. America, N. Asia.

Notes:

## 120. Lapland Rhododendron

*Rhododendron lapponicum* (L.) Wg.

Under-shrub, usually prostrate. Flowers in June shortly after the snow has melted, rarely in July. Leaves coriaceous, covered with rust-coloured hairs beneath. Slightly fragrant when rubbed.

Dry exposed ridges and heaths, gravelly frostheaving soil, often dominant (*Rhododendron*-heath), only on calcareous soils. Bicentric. In S. Norway only in Vågå, Lom, Skjåk and Grytten (Jotunheimen) to 1500 m. In the north from Lycksele Lappmark to Porsanger. Lycksele Lappmark 1320 m. Troms 1060 m.

West-arctic, Scandinavia, N. Finland, Greenland, arctic America, NE. Asia.

119

120

## 121. Blue Mountain-heath

*Phyllodoce caerulea* (L.) Bab.

10—20 cm. July. Evergreen shrub, leaves coriaceous, with a hairy furrow beneath. Flowers red in bud, later purple and finally blue, rarely white. Flower stalks, sepals and capsule glandular.

Preferably found in bilberry-heaths, where it may be abundant. Avoids shady and exposed localities. Descending to the coniferous forests and in some places to the lowland. Throughout the mountains, very common. Jotunheimen 1850 m. Troms 1400 m.

N. Europe, a single locality in Scotland, very rare in the Alps and Pyrenees, Greenland, N. America, N. Asia.

Notes:

## 122. Black Bearberry

*Arctostaphylos alpina* (L.) Spreng.

Flowers early (May—June) as soon as the snow is gone. Prostrate, leaves withering in autumn, but persisting to next summer. The autumn colour is gorgeous red. Fruits at first green, then red, finally when ripe shining black.

Exposed ridges and heaths with *Loiseleuria* and *Diapensia*. Throughout the mountains, very common. Galdhøpiggen 1625 m. Troms 1100 m.

Europe, Greenland, arctic N. America, N. and C. Asia.

Bearberry *(A. uva-ursi)* has coriaceous, evergreen leaves. Fruits red, glossy, without taste. Dry heaths. Throughout Scandinavia. Glittertind 1840 m. Troms 900 m. Europe, N. America, N. and C. Asia.

121 122

### 123. Mossy Mountain-heather

*Cassiope hypnoides* (L.) Don

5 cm. July—Aug. Under-shrub with slender, moss-like branches. Leaves evergreen, pliant, acute. One of the most attractive mountain plants.

Particularly on non-irrigated snow beds, usually in company with Least Willow (no. 45). May predominate together with grey liverworts on solifluction soil where the surface dries up in summer, becoming almost crustaceous. On acid as well as on base-rich soils.

Throughout the mountains, very common. Jotunheimen 1870 m. Troms 1460 m.

Arctic Europe, Greenland, northeastern N. America.

### 124. White Arctic Bell-heather

*Cassiope tetragona* (L.) Don

10—30 cm. July. Stems with hard, scale-like leaves in 4 ranks. Usually the petals are white with pink lobes, anthers pink, flower stalks and sepals red, but the petals may also be yellowish-white, anthers brownish-yellow, flower stalks and sepals yellowish-green. Fragrance somewhat oppressive. Ridges and heaths, preferably on calcareous soils. In many places the predominating species covering large areas, especially on north-facing low-alpine slopes.

Northern unicentric. Saltdal and Pite Lappmark—Porsanger. Torne Lappmark 1647 m.

The arctic parts of Europe, America and Asia. In Greenland important as fuel.

123

124

## 125. Lapland Diapensia

*Diapensia lapponica* L.

2—5 cm. June—July. Stout, deepstriking tap-root. Tufts densely packed, leaves coriaceous, evergreen. The old leaves commonly dark-spotted by a small crustaceous lichen only found on Diapensia.

Grows on the most exposed ridges that are very dry in summer and with a sparse snowcover in winter. It forms a characteristic plant community together with Loiseleuria, Black Bearberry and small crustaceous lichens.

Valdres—Finnmark, common. Sylene 1600 m. Troms 1300 m.

N. Europe, Greenland, arctic N. America, Siberia.

Notes:

## 126. Purple Gentian

*Gentiana purpurea* L.

20—50 cm. Aug. Thick rootstock and roots with a bitter taste. Previously used for medicinal purposes and exported to other Scandinavian countries. Stem stout. Leaves similar to Lily-of-the-Valley. Corolla 3—4 cm, yellow at base. Stamens epipetalous.

Birch forests, willow thickets and subalpine meadows, in moist places. Main distribution Agder and Telemark — Sogn. Scattered to S. Trøndelag. Previously more widely distributed. Hardangervidda 1320 m. Besides known only from the Alps and the Appenines.

125 126

## 127. Scandinavian Primrose

*Primula scandinavica* H. Bruun

5—10 cm, after flowering 15—20 cm. June—July. Leaves glabrous above, with white meal below (crystals secreted from glandular hairs). Flowers 2—10. Calyx divided to the middle.

Grassy hills, ledges. *Dryas*-heaths, only on calcareous soils. Slightly bicentric. Telemark —Jämtland. N. Trøndelag—Varanger. Hardangervidda 1500 m. Troms 680 m. Only in Scandinavia. A very closely related species, *P. scotica*, in Scotland and Orkney.

## 128. Strict Primrose

*Primula stricta* Hornem.

10—20 cm. June—July. Stems more slender than by no. 127. Leaves without meal. Flowers normally 2—4. Calyx divided to a third. Moist places by lakes and brooks, ledges, preferably on base-rich soils. Dovre—Varanger, rare. Lule Lappmark 1120 m.

N. Europe, Greenland, arctic N. America.

Finnmark Primrose (*P. nutans*) grows on salt marshes in Finnmark and by the Gulf of Bothnia. Flowers larger, leaves ovate.

## 129. Field Gentian

*Gentianella campestris* (L.) Börner ssp. *islandica* Murb.

5—15 cm. June—Aug. Flowers violet, often white, rarely yellowish-white. Two broad and two narrow calyx-lobes. Variable species. Grassy hills and meadows. Setesdal —North Cape, not in the eastern mountains of N. Norway. Hardangervidda 1400 m. Troms 450 m.

Europe.

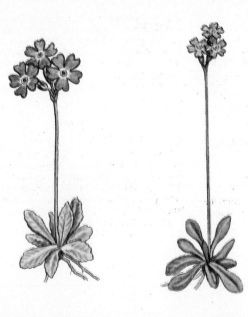

127          128          129

### 130. Snow Gentian

*Gentiana nivalis* L.

5—15 cm. July—Aug. Flowers rarely white. Very sensitive to temperature changes, the petals closing spirally when the temperature goes below +10°C. At lower temperatures the species is not easily noticed.

Grassland, meadows, birch forests, river banks. Throughout the mountains, common. Jotunheimen 1880 m. Troms 1225 m.

Europe, Asia Minor, Greenland, eastern N. America.

### 131. Slender Gentian

*Gentianella tenella* (Rottb.) Börner

3—8 cm. July—Aug. Branched from the base, branches arcuate-erect. Flowers 4-merous. On exposed ridges tiny and one-flowered. *Dryas*-heaths, ridges and rocks, only on base-rich soils. Slightly bicentric, quite rare. Hardangervidda—Trollheimen and Härjedalen. N. Jämtland—Alta. S. Norway 1500 m. Troms 1100 m.

Europe, Greenland, N. America, N. and C. Asia, Atlas.

### 132. Felwort

*Gentianella amarella* (L.) Börner

5—15 cm. July—Aug. Resembles no. 129, but more slender and the calyx-lobes equal. Flowers rarely white. Damp meadows and slopes. In the mountains from Hallingdal to Jämtland, further north to Alta. In the lowlands another race. S. Norway 1200 m.

Europe, N. and C. Asia.

130     131   132

### 133. Jacob's Ladder

*Polemonium caeruleum* L.

30—70 cm. July. Leaves pinnate, ca. 10 pairs of lateral, acute leaflets. Flowers 1,5 cm diam., fragrant. Slopes, willow thickets and grassy scree soil. In the mountains from Hardangervidda to Varanger, and also in many places in the lowlands, but most likely introduced as a garden-escape. S. Norway 1200 m. Lofoten 520 m.

Europe, N. and C. Asia.

Acutish Jacob's Ladder *(P. acutiflorum)* is more slender, the lobes of the corolla acute; the upper part of the stem, flower-stalks and sepals with woolly hairs. Pite Lappmark—Varanger, rare.

Boreal Jacob's Ladder *(P. boreale)*, 10—15 cm, woolly and glandular-hirsute, foetid. Varanger.

Notes:

### 134. Mountain Forget-me-not

*Myosotis decumbens* Host.

20—30 cm. July. Stems branched, leaves with spreading hairs. Vegetative reproduction by means of leafy and rooting stolons from the lowermost axils. Corolla-lobes flat, ca. 1 cm diam. Calyx with hooked hairs on the tube. At an early stage the petals are red, changing gradually to blue (rarely white).

Birch forests, willow thickets, grassy slopes rich in moisture and mould. Throughout the mountains, common. Jotunheimen 1660 m. Troms 1100 m.

N. and C. Europe.

133

134

## 135. Rock Speedwell

*Veronica fruticans* Jacq.

5—10 cm. July—Aug. One of the most attractive mountain plants. Under-shrub with
stock and lower stem woody, the only *Veronica* in Scandinavia of this type. Petals rarely
white or pink. Flowering of short duration,
often only one day. The white anthers and the
purplish ring in the middle of the flower may
guide insects to the nectaries. Blackens when
dried.

Ledges, heaths, most abundantly on south-
facing scree slopes, preferably on base-rich
soils. Throughout the mountains, quite common. On south-facing slopes at lower altitudes
as well. Jotunheimen 1800 m. Troms 1000 m.

Europe, Greenland.

Notes:

## 136. Alpine Speedwell

*Veronica alpina* L.

5—15 cm. July—Aug. The petals rarely
white or reddish, the flowers closed during
rainy weather. Capsule bluish green, glabrous.
A form with hairy capsule is regarded as iden-
tical with the middle-European *V. pumila*.
Blackens when dried.

Moist meadows, grassland, snow beds,
by brooks, on acid as well as on base-rich
soils. Throughout the mountains, very common, in the north descending to the lowland.
Jotunheimen 2000 m. Troms 1300 m.

Scandinavia, N. Russia, Scotland, the
Faroes, Iceland, Greenland, NE. Canada.

Slender Speedwell *(V. tenella).* Stems prostrate, flowers bluish-white, raceme glandular-
pubescent. N. Trøndelag—Finnmark. Distribution uncertain.

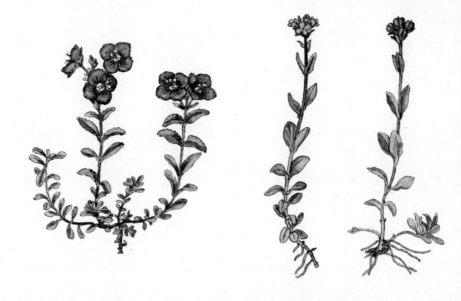

135                                    136

### 137. Mountain Eyebright

*Euphrasia frigida* Pugsl.

3—10 cm. July—Aug. The genus *Euphrasia* is a very critical one with many minor races and hybrides. Parasitic on the roots of other plants. The Mountain Eyebright has pubescent stems, small flowers and ciliate capsules exceeding the sepals. Meadows, heaths and fens. Throughout the mountains, very common, Jotunheimen 1800 m. Troms 1060 m.

Scandinavia, N. Russia, Scotland, the Faroes, Iceland, Greenland, NE. Canada.

Lapland Eyebright *(E. lapponica)* has completely glabrous capsules. Dry localities on limestone and schists. Bicentric. Hardanger —Trollheimen, very rare. More common from Bindal to Finnmark. Trollheimen 1300 m. Known only from Scandinavia. Close relatives in Gotland, Ireland, and the Alps.

Notes:

### 138. Alpine Bartsia

*Bartsia alpina* L.

20—30 cm. July—Aug. Underground creeping rhizome with several stems. Parasiting on grasses. Inflorescence glandular. Rarely the flowers may be yellow (f. *ochroleuca),* whereas the bracts are green. Blackens when dried.

Damp meadows, fens, willow thickets, birch forests, most frequently on base-rich soils.

Throughout the mountains, very common. Jotunheimen 1960 m. Troms 1120 m. In W. and N. Norway descending to sea level, in E. Norway to the valleys. Two isolated localities in S. Sweden (Östergötland and Gotland).

Europe, Greenland, NE. Canada.

137

138

## 139. Sceptred Lousewort

*Pedicularis sceptrum-carolinum* L.

30—60 cm. July—Aug. Large rosette of leaves. Several rigid stems from the stock, often without leaves. The corolla is completely closed, pollinated by big insects such as bumble bees which are able to squeeze the lips apart. The name is given to honour the Swedish King, Charles XII.

Moist localities, meadows, fens, willow thickets. In the mountains from Telemark to Varanger, in S. Norway only in the eastern parts. In Sweden and N. Norway in the lowland as well. S. Norway 1200 m. Troms 500 m.

Europe, N. Asia.

Notes:

## 140. Lapland Lousewort

*Pedicularis lapponica* L.

10—20 cm. July—Aug. Slender, straight stems from a creeping rhizome. Flowers rose-scented. The lower lip twisted into a vertical position. The fruit is a capsule horizontally arranged. It opens in its upper end forming a shovel. If the shovel is pushed from above, the seeds fall down into it, and when the elastic flower stalks springs back, the seeds are thrown out.

In damp meadows as well as on dry heaths. Setesdal—Varanger, very common. Jotunheimen 1700 m. Troms 1300 m.

N. Europe, Greenland, arctic N. America, N. Asia.

139

140

## 141. Hairy Lousewort

*Pedicularis hirsuta* L.

5—15 cm. July. The upper part of the stem and the calyx woolly. Moist localities, mountain tops, partly also on snow beds and especially on solifluction soil'on north-facing slopes, particularly on base-rich soils. Northern unicentric. Saltdal and Pite Lappmark—Alta, rare. Troms 1380 m.

Greenland, the arctic parts of Europe, America and Asia.

All species of the genus *Pedicularis* are partial parasites. They have suckers on the roots, and by means of these they attach themselves to other plants, e.g. to Dwarf Birch, from which they absorb food.

## 142. Oeder's Lousewort

*Pedicularis oederi* Vahl

10—20 cm. June—Aug. Stem thick, both the stem and the pedicels remain elastic until next summer and the seed dispersal is similar to that of the Lapland Lousewort (no. 140). The uppermost flowers come out first. Dry as well as moist localities, heaths, meadows, fens, often abundant, particularly on base-rich soils. In fens descending to the coniferous region. Southern unicentric. Hardangervidda—Snåsa and N. Jämtland. Jotunheimen 1960 m.

Europe, arctic N. America, N. and C. Asia. Isolated in Scandinavia.

Notes:

141
142

### 143. Flame-tipped Lousewort

*Pedicularis flammea* L.

5—10 cm. July—Aug. Stem thinner than by Oeder's Lousewort, glabrous. Spike narrow, few-flowered. Style not protruding, auto-pollination seems to be the normal situation.

Meadows, heaths, solifluction soil and moist gravel on base-rich soils. Northern unicentric, very rare, but in some localities abundant. Saltdal and Pite Lappmark — N. Troms. Lule Lappmark 1320 m. Troms 1295 m.

Iceland, Greenland and the eastern parts of arctic N. America.

### 144. Bog Whortleberry

*Vaccinium uliginosum* L.

Variabel. In bogs at low altitudes ¾ m, in exposed places in the mountains depressed. Leaves somewhat leathery, but deciduos. Corolla urceolate, white-yellowish, white or pinkish. The berries edible, not as sweet as the bilberries, but very useful, especially for juice. Bogs, dwarf birch thickets and even on exposed ridges. Jotunheimen 1730 m. Troms 1060 m.

Europe, N. Asia, N. America.

143 144

## 145. Common Butterwort

*Pinguicula vulgaris* L.

6—12 cm. Leaves fleshy, clothed with sticky glands which catch small insects. The glands produce an enzyme-containing secretion which decomposes the insect's protein. The products of digestion are absorbed by the plant. The secretion also causes milk to curdle. In popular medicine used as a bleaching agent for hair. Rarely the whole flower or only the lower lip may be white.

Preferably on moist mossy localities, fens, springs, ledges, but also in dry places, i.a. *Dryas*-heaths. Throughout Scandinavia, common. Jotunheimen 1700 m. Troms 910 m.

Europe, Greenland, N. America, N. and E. Asia, N. Africa.

Notes:

## 146. Alpine Butterwort

*Pinguicula alpina* L.

6—12 cm. July—Aug. Moist places on base-rich soils, often in great abundance. Fens, hillsides, ledges, particularly on solifluction soil on north-facing slopes. Bicentric. In S. Scandinavia only from Kvikne to NW. Härjedalen. In the north from Hattfjelldal and Åsele Lappmark to Varanger. Also in Gotland. Dovre 1150 m. Troms 1000 m.

Europe, N. and C. Asia.

Hairy Butterwort *(P. villosa)*. 5 cm. Rosette leaves brownish. Flowers 7 mm, pale violet with two yellow spots on the lower lip. Grows only on compact tussocks of peat mosses *(Sphagnum fuscum),* usually in the forest region, but quite frequently also above the timber line. Eastern distribution. Valdres—Varanger.

145                          146

## 147. Harebell or Bluebell

### *Campanula rotundifolia* L.

10—20 cm. July—Aug. Variable species. The common mountain race differs from the lowland race in having short, unbranched stems with a single terminal flower. The length of the bell up to 3 cm. Capsule nodding, opening by basal pores, cf. no. 148. In the north a race with pale blue flowers occurs.

Heaths, ridges and ledges. Throughout the mountains, common. Jotunheimen 2100 m. Troms 1120 m.

Europe, Greenland, N. America, N. and C. Asia.

Notes:

## 148. Arctic Harebell

### *Campanula uniflora* L.

5—10 cm. July—Aug. Our smallest bluebell. Tap-root thick, striking deep. The bell less than 1 cm. When ripe the stems and the flower stalks straighten and become stiff. The capsules are erect, ca. 2 cm, opening by pores at the top. The seeds are thrown out by means of the wind, the elastic stems acting as a catapult for hurling them.

Dry exposed ridges and tops. *Dryas*-heaths on base-rich and schisty soils. Bicentric (see map p. 12), rare. Jotunheimen—Trollheimen. Åsele Lappmark—Nordreisa. Jotunheimen 1810 m. Troms 1390 m.

West-arctic. N. Europe, N. America, E. Siberia.

147                            148

## 149. Golden-rod

*Solidago virgaurea* L.

10—40 cm. July—Aug. Variable species. The mountain race has strongly pubescent stems and stalks, basal leaves slightly toothed. In the birch region the species is taller, the upper part of the stems sparsely pubescent, basal leaves toothed. Birch forests, willow thickets, undershrub- and grassheaths. Throughout Scandinavia, common. Jotunheimen 2090 m. Troms 1100 m.

Europe, Asia, N. Africa.

## 150. Shining Fleabane

*Erigeron politum* Fr.

20—50 cm. July. Stems and leaves almost glabrous. Bracts dark-violet (The lowland species Blue Fleabane *(E. acris)* is pubescent, bracts paler). Ledges and grassy slopes in the birch region and a short distance above the timber-line. Sogn and Gudbrandsdalen—Finnmark. Belongs to a critical group and is known only from Scandinavia and the Kola Peninsula.

## 151. Dwarf Fleabane

*Erigeron uniflorum* L.

5—15 cm, at the initial flowering time often only 1—2 cm. July—Aug. Leaves hairy along the margins. Disk-flowers yellow, gradually becoming red-tipped. Ray-flowers white, becoming purplish. Snow beds and mountain plateaus on easily disintegrating rocks. Setesdal—Varanger, common. Jotunheimen 2120 m. Troms 1440 m.

Europe, Greenland, N. America, N. and C. Asia.

Boreal Fleabane *(E. boreale).* 15—25 cm. Between the ray-flowers and the inner hermaphrodite disk-flower a row of female disk-flowers. Leaves hairy. Meadows, scree slopes, preferably on calcareous soils. Setesdal—Finnmark. West-arctic.

149 150 151

## 152. Black Fleabane

*Erigeron humilis* Grah.

5—12 cm. July—Aug. Leaves hairy, stems and bracts with dark hairs. Ray-flowers white, changing gradually to purple or blue. Damp localities, snow beds, solifluction soil, on calcareous soils. Northern unicentric. Åsele Lappmark and Saltdal—Finnmark, rare. Troms 1400 m.

N. Europe, Greenland, N. America, Siberia.

## 153. Alpine Cat's Foot

*Antennaria alpina* (L.) Gaertn.

5—12 cm. July—Aug. Sexes on different plants. Male plant very rare. Reproduction by seeds not resulting from a sexual fusion. Pappus white, rarely red. Basal leaves pubescent above, woolly beneath, bracts greyish-brown. In Cat's Foot *(A. dioeca)* which also occurs frequently in the mountains, the basal leaves are glabrous above and white-woolly beneath, bracts white or pink.

*A. alpina* grows on top-plateaus and on heaths of grasses and under-shrubs. Throughout the mountains, common. Male plant bicentric. Jotunheimen 2250 m. Troms 1430 m.

N. Europe, Greenland, N. America.

Porsild's Cat's Foot *(A. porsildii)* is almost glabrous, stems slender with a few heads. Northern unicentric. Pite Lappmark—N. Troms. Besides only Greenland.

## 154. Carpathian Fleabane

*Antennaria carpatica* (Wg.) Bl. & Fing.

10—20 cm. July—Aug. More highgrown than no. 153. Basal leaves 3-veined. Female plants with long silky pappus. Late-exposed meadows, ledges, on calcareous soils. Northern unicentric, rare. Lule Lappmark 1440 m. Troms 1200 m.

Europe, N. America, arctic Siberia.

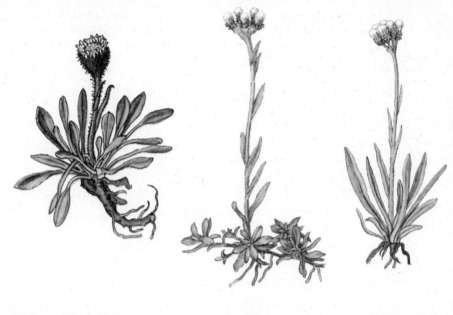

152               153               154

## 155. Dwarf Cudweed

### *Gnaphalium supinum* L.

2—8 cm. July—Aug. In small tufts from a creeping stock. Leaves, stems and bracts woolly. When the fruits are ripe the bracts spread out, forming a star.

One of the commonest species in snow beds. In late exposed, non-irrigated snow beds it may be so abundant on slopes that they become grey-coloured. Also on paths, solifluction soil and mountain plateaus. Preferably on acid soils.

Throughout the mountains, very common. Jotunheimen 2000 m. Troms 1270 m.

Europe, Greenland, NE. Canada, Ural, Asia Minor.

Notes:

## 156. Highland Cudweed

### *Gnaphalium norvegicum* Gunn.

15—30 cm. July—Aug. Stems stiff from a short stock. The whole plant covered with silvery-grey woolly hairs. Leaves lanceolate, the lower one with a distrinct mid-vein and two less distrinct lateral veins. Heads with outer male flowers, inner flowers hermaphrodite.

Birch forests, willow thickets, bilberry heaths and early exposed grassy snow beds. Throughout the mountains, common. Jotunheimen 1780 m. Troms 1120 m.

Europe, Greenland, NE. Canada. Caucasus, C. Asia.

Wood Cudweed *(G. sylvaticum)* ascends to the birch region. Bracts paler. Stemleaves with only a single vein.

155                              156

## 157. Norwegian Wormwood

*Artemisia norvegica* Th. Fr.

10—25 cm. Aug. Tufted. Heads few, often only one, stalks woolly-hairy. Rootstock very stout. Dry exposed ridges and tops, scree slopes. Descending to the lowland (Sunndalen) along rivers, growing on gravel banks.

Southern unicentric. From Folldal north to Surnadal, Rindal and Rennebu, west to the Sunndal Mts. Ryfylke. Besides only known from Ural and Scotland. Often it occurs very abundantly, particularly on mineral soil and on calcareous rocks. Trollheimen 1640 m. The Scottish plant is described as a subspecies of its own.

Notes:

## 158. Alpine Arnica

*Arnica alpina* (L.) Olin

10—20 cm. July—Aug. Leaves, stems and bracts hairy. Usually only one head, ca. 3 cm diameter. Dry ridges and rocks, *Dryas*-heaths, ledges, gravel bars, only on calcareous soils. Northern unicentric, rare. Pite Lappmark and Saltdal—Varanger. Lule Lappmark 1440 m. Troms 1200 m.

This race is known only from the northern part of Norway, Sweden and Finland, and also the Kola Peninsula. It is closely related to other races with its nearest localities in Spitzbergen, Novaya Zemlya and North Ural.

157

158

## 159. Alpine Saussurea

*Saussurea alpina* (L.) DC.

10—30 cm. July—Aug. Creeping stock with short stolons. Stems stout, erect. Leaves white-cottony beneath. Above the timber line usually with few heads, but in sheltered localities in the birch region with several. The flowers vanilla-scented.

Birch forests, willow thickets, fens, meadows and heaths, in snow beds often in abundance, but sterile, preferably on calcareous soils. Throughout the mountains, common, and in the lowland as well. Postglacial relic in S. Sweden. Jotunheimen 2130 m. Troms 1380 m.

Europe, Closely related species in Siberia and arctic. N. America.

Notes:

## 160. Autumnal Hawkbit

*Leontodon autumnalis* L.

7—15 cm. July—Sept. Resembles Hawkweeds *(Hieracium),* but the pappus is feathery (in Hawkweeds simple, fragile bristles). Critical, very variable species. The mountain race (var. *taraxaci* (L.) Rouy) differs from the lowland races in lower growth, single-flowered, bracts black and strongly woolly, stems hairy, basal leaves entire with few teeth or somewhat pinnatifid. The plant contains milky juice.

Grassland, particularly on grassy snow beds. In the willow thickets and the birch region other forms. Throughout Scandinavia, very common. Jotunheimen 1600 m. Troms 1040 m.

Europe, NW. Africa, Asia, Greenland.

159

160

### 161. Melancholy Thistle

*Cirsium heterophyllum* (L.) Hill

½—1 m (1½ m). July—Aug. Stems stout, grooved, pubescent in the upper leafless part. Basal leaves entire, long-stalked, lanceolate, lowest stem-leaves sometimes pinnatifid, all leaves with prickly margins, glabrous above, white-felted beneath. Heads more than 2 cm diam. Rarely the flowers may be white.

One of the characteristic species of the sub-alpine birch forest also in willow thickets, on scree slopes and by brooks. Throughout Scandinavia, common. Jotunheimen 1680 m. Troms 1115 m.

Europe, N. Asia.


Notes:

### 162. Blue Sow-thistle

*Lactuca alpina* (L.) A. Gray

1—1½ m. July—Aug. Creeping branched stock. Stems furrowed, hollow, the lower part bristly, the upper part and the stalks glandular-hairy. Upper leaves lanceolate, the lower lyrate-pinnatifid with a large triangular lobe. Heads 2—3 cm diam., rarely white. The whole plant is juicy, and especially when young a delicacy for bears and deer.

Characteristic species of moist humusrich soil in sub-alpine birch forests and on scree slopes. Throughout the mountains and in the lowland as well. S. Norway 1300 m. Troms 1000 m. Known only from Europe.

161 162

## 163. Lapland Butterbur

*Petasites frigidus* (L.) Fr.

Leaves and scapes from a slender, branched, horizontal rhizome. Scapes bearing brown scaly leaves, at times tipped with a small blade. Basal leaves triangular with shallow lobes, glabrous above, white-tomentose beneath. Resembles the leaves of Coltsfoot *(Tussilago farfara),* but has larger and more acute lobes. Dioecious. The scape of the male plant 20—30 cm, that of the female one 25—50 cm. June—July. Male heads pink, apparently hermaphrodite, but only producing pollen. Female heads yellowish-white, fruit with a long silky, soft pappus.

Wet localities, snow beds, fens, by brooks. Telemark—Varanger. Jotunheimen 1750 m. Troms 1380 m.

N. Russia, N. Siberia, N. America.

## 164. Alpine Hawkweed

*Hieracium alpinum* L.

10—15 cm. July—Aug. The whole genus is very critical, from Scandinavia alone about 2000 minor species having been described. Many of these are found in the mountains. Most of the *Hieracium*-species produce seeds without sexual fusion, but some have normal sexual reproduction and may hybridize. The Alpine Hawkweed has usually a single small stem-leaf. Leaves, stems as well as bracts with hairs and small glands, the latter visible by means of a hand-lens.

Particularly on ridges and heaths. Throughout the mountains, very common. Jotunheimen 1960 m. Troms 1160 m.

Europe, Greenland.

Notes:

163             164

# INDEX

Aconitum 82
Alchemilla 112
Alpine Poa 32
Alpine Saussurea 164
Anemone 88
Angelica 124
Antennaria 158
Anthoxanthum 28
Anthyllis 118
Arabis 92
Arctostaphylos 130
Arenaria 72
Arnica 162
Artemisia 162
Asphodel 52
Asplenium 24
Astragalus 114, 116
Athyrium 24
Avens 110
Bartsia 144
Bearberry 130
Bell-heather 132

Betula 64
Birch 64
Bluebell 154
Botrychium 22
Bramble 106
Braya 94
Butterbur 168
Buttercup 84, 86
Butterwort 152
Campanula 154
Campion 68, 78
Cardamine 92
Cardaminopsis 94
Carex 36—44
Cassiope 132
Catchfly 80
Cat's Foot 158
Cerastium 74
Chamorchis 52
Chickweed 74
Cinquefoil 108
Cirsium 166

Cloudberry 106
Clubmoss 20
Coeloglossum 54
Cornus 124
Cotton-grass 34
Cranesbill 118
Cress 92
Cryptogramma 24
Cudweed 160
Deschampsia 30
Diapensia 134
Draba 90
Dryas 110
Dwarf Birch 64
Dwarf Cornel 124
Epilobium 120, 122
Equisetum 22
Erigeron 156
Eriophorum 34
Euphrasia 144
Eyebright 144
False Orchid 52

Felwort 136
Fleabane 156, 158
Forget-me-not 140
Fragrant Orchid 52
Frog Orchid 54
Gentiana 134, 138
Gentianella 138
Geranium 118
Globe Flower 82
Gnaphalium 160
Golden-rod 156
Grape-fern 22
Grass of Parnassus 106
Gymnadenia 52
Hair-grass 30
Harebell 154
Hare's-tail 34
Hawkbit 164
Hawkweed 168
Hieracium 168
Holly Fern 26
Horsetail 22
Iceland Koenigia 66
Jacob's Ladder 140
Juncus 46
Kidney-vetch 118
Knotweed 66

Kobresia 34
Koenigia 66
Lactuca 166
Lady-fern 24
Lady's Mantle 112
Leontodon 164
Leucorchis 54
Loiseleuria 128
Lousewort 146—150
Luzula 48
Lychnis 78
Lycopodium 20
Meadow Rue 80
Melandrium 78
Milk-vetch 114, 116
Minuartia 70, 72
Monkshood 82
Moonwort 22
Moss Campion 68
Mountain Avens 110
Mountain-heath 130
Mountain Queen 98
Mountain-Saxifrage 102
Mountain Sorrel 64
Myosotis 140
Nigritella 54
Orchid 52, 54

Oxyria 64
Oxytropis 116
Papaver 88
Parnassia 106
Parsley Fern 24
Pearlwort 68
Pedicularis 146—150
Petasites 168
Phippsia 32
Phleum 28
Phyllodoce 130
Pinguicula 152
Poa 32
Polemonium 140
Polygonum 66
Polystichum 26
Poppy 88
Potentilla 108
Primrose 136
Primula 136
Pyrola 126
Ranunculus 84, 86
Rhododendron 128
Rock-cress 92, 94
Roegneria 30
Rose-root 96
Rubus 106

Rush 46
Sagina 68
Salix 56—62
Sandwort 70—72
Saussurea 164
Saxifraga 98—104
Scented Nigritella 54
Sedge 36—44
Sedum 96
Sibbaldia 110
Silene 68
Snow Grass 32
Solidago 156
Sorrel 64

Sow-thistle 166
Speedwell 142
Spleenwort 24
Spring Pasque Flower 88
Stag's-Horn Moss 20
Starwort 76
Stellaria 76
Stonecrop 96
Thalictrum 80
Thistle 166
Timothy 28
Tofieldia 52
Trisetum 30
Trollius 82

Vaccinium 150
Vernal-grass 28
Veronica 142
Viola 120
Violet 120
Wheat-grass 30
Whitlow-grass 90
Whortleberry 150
Willow 56—62
Willow-herb 120, 122
Wintergreen 126
Woodrush 48
Woodsia 26
Wormwood 162

# GLOSSARY

Achene — a small dry single-seeded fruit which does not split open.

Acute — ending in a point.

Anther — the part of a stamen containing the pollen-grains.

Arcuate — curved like an arc.

Axile — the angle between a leaf and the stem.

Bicentric — see p. 12.

Bifid — cleft in two.

Bifurcate — twice forked.

Bract — small leaf, ususally subtending a flower.

Calyx — the set of outermost members of a flower, usually green.

Capitate — head-like.

Chromosome — the microscopic rod-like structures found within living cells and carrying the determiners of hereditary characters. The number of chromosomes are constant for each species.

Ciliate — with hairs along the margin.

Cordate — heart-shaped.

Coriaceous — leathery.

Crenate, crenulate — having rounded teeth.

Cuneiform — wedge-shaped.

Cyme — a type of inflorescence in which the main stem ends in a flower, as do successive branches, and in which each terminal flower is usually overtopped by branches.

Deciduous — with leaves falling off at the end of the season.

Deflexed — bent sharply downwards.

Dioecious — with either male or female flowers.

Endemic — native only in one country or other small area.

Filament — the stalk of a stamen.

Filiform — thread-like, very slender.

Flexuous — wavy.

Glabrous — hairless, smooth.

Glaucous — blue-green.

Glumes — the lowest pair of scales in the spikelets of grasses.

Hirsute — clothed with longish hairs.

Hyaline — thin and translucent.

Inflorescence — flower-cluster.

Lacerate — irregularly divided as though torn.

Lanceolate — lance-shaped.

Lax — loosely branched or aggregated.

Leguminous — belonging to the pea family.

Lemma — the bract of a grass flower.

Ligulate — strap-shaped.

Lyrate — lyre-shaped, leaves with a terminal lobe much larger than the lateral lobes.

Membranous — thin and flexible, not green.

Monoecious — with separate male and female flowers, but with both kinds on the same plant.

Obtuse — blunt-ended.

Orbicular — circular in outline.

Palmate — with lobes diverging from a common centre, more or less like the fingers of a hand.

Panicle — a branched inflorescence.

Pappus — the tuft of hairs on the fruits of many members of the daisy family: thistledown.

Pedicel — the stalk of a single flower.

Peduncle — the stalk of a flower-cluster.

Perianth — the floral leaves.

Persistent — remaining attached even after dying and withering.

Petiole — leaf-stalk.

Phanerogam — plant with seeds.

Pinnae — the leaflets of a pinnate leaf.

Pinnate — a leaf with leaflets arranged either side of a common stalk.

Pinnatifid — leaf pinnately lobed.

Procumbent — lying along the surface of the ground.

Pubescent — shortly and softly hairy.

Raceme — an elongated inflorescence with a main axis along which single flowers are arranged, cf. spike.

Reticulate — net-veined.

Rhachis — the main stalk of a fern leaf on which the leaflets are born.

Rhizome — a persistent underground stem, usually growing more or less horizontally.

Rugose — wrinkled.

Scabrous — rough to the touch.

Serrate — toothed like a saw.

Serrulate — with small teeth.

Solifluction — the downhill «flowing» of wet soil and stones after the surface has thawed in spring.

Sorus — a cluster of sporangia.

Sporangium — the spore-containing organs in ferns, club-mosses, horse-tails, etc.

Staminode — a stamen-like organ which does not produce pollen.

Stellate — star-shaped.

Stigma — the sticky top of the style to which pollen grains adhere.

Stipule — scaly or leafy appendage at the base of a leaf-stalk.

Stoloniferous — having creeping stems, either above or below the ground surface.

Ternate — term used of a leaf divided into 3 more or less equal parts.

Tomentose — with short and dense cottony hairs.

Tortuose — bent or twisted.

Trifoliate — term used of a leaf with 3 leaflets.

Tuberculate — with knobbly projections.

Unicentric — see p. 12.

Viscid — sticky.

Viviparous — with the flowers growing out into young plantlets or replaced by such plantlets, no seeds being formed.